PRENTICE HALL
WORLD STUDIES

AYP Monitoring
Assessments

PEARSON

Prentice
Hall

Needham, Massachusetts
Upper Saddle River, New Jersey

The maps on pages 139, 141, 143, 173, 189, 190, 195, 200, 206, 208, 209, and 212 are based on maps created by **DK Cartography.**

ISBN 0-13-128094-5
3 4 5 6 7 8 9 10   08 07 06 05

Table of Contents

How to Use This Book

World Studies AYP Monitoring Assessments provides a clear path to *adequate yearly progress* through systematic testing and recommendations for remediation. Progress monitoring at regular intervals ensures that students understand key content before moving on in the course. With the results of these tests, you will know when to modify instruction because a class is having difficulty and when to assign remediation because individual students need more help.

Beginning the Year: Establishing the Baseline

Teaching for adequate yearly progress (AYP) begins with evaluating student strengths and weaknesses. Before launching into the curriculum, you need to know how well your students read and how proficient they are in social studies skills. Use the following tests to measure student readiness for your course.

Screening Tests (pages 1–11)

Administer a Screening Test to evaluate students' ability to read the textbook. These tests identify students who are reading two or more years below grade level. You may wish to consider placing them in intensive intervention. For students with lesser difficulties, you can use the recommendations for Differentiated Instruction in the Teacher's Edition of your textbook.

Diagnosing Readiness Tests (pages 13–63)

The Diagnosing Readiness Tests measure your students' abilities in skills essential to success in social studies. There are two tests in each of the following categories:

- Geographic Literacy
- Visual Analysis
- Critical Thinking and Reading
- Communications
- Vocabulary
- Writing

Once you have test results, consult the correlation table in this book to locate program resources for instruction and practice in individual skills. Repeat these tests as least once more during the year to gauge student progress and identify skills needing improvement.

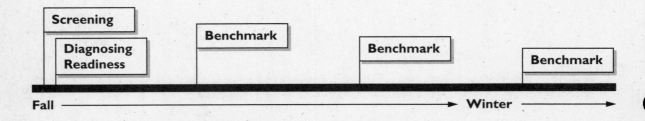

Monitoring Progress Over the Year

The section and chapter assessments in the Student Edition and Teaching Resources measure understanding of what students have learned on a short-term basis. To measure student retention over time, it is important to administer benchmark tests and refocus instruction based on test results.

Benchmark Tests (pages 81–152)

Benchmark testing is at the heart of progress monitoring and student achievement. At specified intervals throughout the year, give Benchmark Tests to evaluate student progress toward mastery of essential content. All questions on the Benchmark Tests correlate to core standards established for this course. See standards on pages 78–79.

Critical to student achievement is analyzing benchmark tests results to adapt your teaching to student needs. Item tallies will show you areas where the whole class is having difficulty and thus merit reteaching. Items with just a few incorrect answers indicate that only certain students need remediation assignments.

Report Sheets (pages 153–169)

The student Benchmark Test report sheet identifies

- test items by number
- correlated standards
- student performance on each test item
- relevant assignments in the *Reading and Vocabulary Study Guide* for remediation of items that students have missed

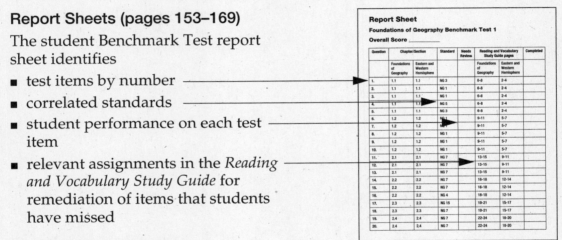

Ending the Year

Modifying your teaching as indicated by the results of the Screening, Diagnosing Readiness, and Benchmark tests throughout the school year, sets the stage for your students to achieve adequate yearly progress.

Outcome Tests (pages 170–225)

Administer the Outcome Tests to see how well students have mastered course content. Like the Benchmark Tests, Outcome Test items are correlated to course standards.

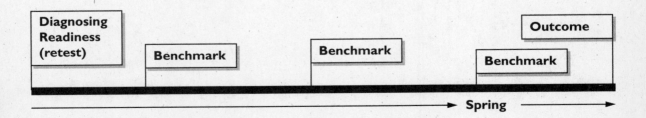

Grade 6 Screening Test

Directions: *Read each passage and answer the questions that follow it. Mark the letter of the best answer to each question.*

On the first day of art class, Ms. Rodak gave some unusual homework. "I'd like you to look at everyday objects with new eyes," she said. "Look at these things as though you've never seen them before."

When she went home that day, Trudy walked through different rooms of her house. She studied the carpet and the wallpaper. She noticed that the living room ceiling was a different color from the walls. There was a painting of vegetables in a wagon on one of the walls. It had hung there since Trudy was a baby, but she never had paid attention to it before.

"Mom?" Trudy called as she stood mesmerized by the painting. "Where did this come from?"

Trudy's mother came into the room. She said, "Your grandfather painted that for your grandmother." Trudy and her mother stood facing the painting. "I wish you had been able to meet him," Trudy's mother sighed. "You would have gotten along well." She gave Trudy's shoulder a squeeze. "You're an awful lot like him."

"Do you know anything else about the painting?" Trudy asked.

"Well," Trudy's mother said, "I've forgotten what it says, but I believe there's a message on the back. Let's take it down and look."

The message was simple, but Trudy could not believe how perfect it was. The message read: "To my darling wife, who makes me see the world with new eyes."

---

1. Which of these events happened first?
   A. Trudy studied her grandfather's painting.
   B. Trudy read something her grandfather wrote.
   C. Trudy started her homework assignment.
   D. Trudy's mother got home from work.

2. Ms. Rodak's assignment is meant to help students
   A. become smarter.
   B. see things differently.
   C. calm down.
   D. be more responsible.

3. Paragraph 2 is mostly about Trudy's
   A. learning about her grandfather.
   B. puzzling over her homework assignment.
   C. searching for a forgotten message.
   D. looking at something with new eyes.

4. Information in the passage suggests that
   A. Trudy never knew her grandfather.
   B. Trudy's father had to work late.
   C. Trudy's grandfather was famous.
   D. Trudy told Ms. Rodak about the painting.

Grade 6 Screening Test (continued)

The screen door slammed shut as Lewis tossed his backpack on the kitchen table. He opened the refrigerator door and let the cool air pour over him.

"Don't leave the refrigerator door open," his dad hollered. Although it was an order, his voice carried the hint of a smile.

Lewis poured himself a glass of cold milk. He headed down the hall to what his dad called "the home office."

"What's new, Tiger?" Lewis's dad inquired, looking up from a computer. Lewis could always tell when his dad didn't mind being interrupted. This was one of those times.

"I just got my spring schedule," Lewis said. "It will be great—I have Spanish first period, English second, and math third." Lewis took a long gulp of milk before continuing. "Then there's lunch, of course. After that—science, social studies, and gym."

"I see you've arranged for gym at the end of the day again," said Lewis's dad.

"Yup," mumbled Lewis as he wiped the milk mustache from his upper lip. "That way, I can come straight home in my gym clothes and relax."

"Wait a minute. I thought you were talking about going out for tennis this spring."

"Uh, Dad," Lewis said, scrunching up his face. "You were the one talking about it, not me. Give me three good reasons why I should."

"Okay," said Lewis's dad, concentrating hard for a moment. "One—you'll develop a friendship with the other players."

"I already have that with the guys I play with in the city basketball league."

Lewis's dad went on. "Two—it will keep you fit and prevent you from getting bored after school."

"That's only two reasons, but whose counting?"

Lewis's dad could see he was getting nowhere fast. He looked Lewis square in the face and said, "Three—I need a new tennis partner. I've been hoping you'd take up tennis so I wouldn't have to start interviewing someone else."

Lewis melted on the spot. At least he knew why his dad had been pestering him about tennis. "Aw, Dad. Why didn't you say so earlier? Come on, you look like you need a break. I'll pour you a cold glass of milk and then—" he smiled over his left shoulder on his way to the kitchen, "and then we'll go visit the tennis courts."

Grade 6 Screening Test (continued)

5. In this story, what does the author emphasize about Lewis and his father?

   A. their athletic skills

   B. their sense of competition

   C. their stubbornness

   D. their ability to talk to one another

6. How does Lewis's dad know the refrigerator door is open?

   A. He felt the air grow cold.

   B. He left it open himself.

   C. He knows his son's habits.

   D. He works next to the kitchen.

7. When Lewis's dad's voice "carried a hint of a smile," it meant he was

   A. in a good mood.

   B. not very pleased.

   C. trying to sound like someone else.

   D. just about done with his work.

8. Why is Lewis happy about his spring schedule?

   A. His classes sound challenging.

   B. He is excited to learn Spanish.

   C. He can take tennis lessons in gym class.

   D. He can come home and relax after gym class.

9. What does the author mean by "Lewis's dad could see he was getting nowhere fast"?

   A. He needed to get back to work.

   B. He had some errands to run.

   C. He was unable to persuade Lewis.

   D. He needed to find a new partner quickly.

10. What is Lewis's dad's third reason for encouraging Lewis to join the tennis team?

   A. He wants Lewis to stay fit.

   B. He wants Lewis to be his new tennis partner.

   C. He thinks it will help Lewis make friends.

   D. He believes his son will enjoy playing tennis.

11. The sentence "Lewis melted on the spot" suggests that Lewis is

   A. suddenly aware of the heat.

   B. touched by his dad's words.

   C. ready for another glass of milk.

   D. sorry about not liking tennis.

12. What is it about the third reason that affects Lewis the most?

   A. its importance

   B. its surprise

   C. its humor

   D. its honesty

Grade 6 Screening Test (continued)

Bats are unique because they are the only mammals that can fly. Most bats feast on flying insects caught in midair. Some bats, however, choose a different place to find their food: the water. Several types of bats catch fish. They achieve this feat in much the same way all bats find food.

Bats use a technique called "echolocation" to navigate while flying. Since most bats fly at night, they have to get around without using their eyes. Instead, they use their ears. A bat uses the sounds it hears to find its position while flying. The bat will periodically "chirp" or "screech." This high-pitched sound will go out and bounce off of whatever is in front of or around the bat. When the sound waves come back to the bat's incredibly sensitive ears, the bat can tell how close it is to other objects.

One particular fishing bat is called the greater bulldog bat, or just the bulldog bat. It lives in Central and South America, and its favorite cafeterias are ponds, rivers, and even the ocean. As the bulldog bat flies above the surface of the water, it "chirps." The bat can sense the small ripples made by fish swimming close to the surface of the water. When the bulldog bat finds a ripple, it flies past the ripple. Then it comes around for another pass, very close to the surface of the water.

The bulldog bat hangs its feet in the water where it thinks the fish may be swimming. If it catches one, the bat quickly stuffs the fish in its mouth and keeps on hunting. The partially chewed fish is stored in the bat's large cheek pouches. This explains where the bulldog bat got its name. Its wide face with large cheeks and swollen lips looks something like a bulldog.

Bulldog bats are unusual because they can not only fly, but they can also swim. If a bat flies too close to the water's surface or catches a fish that is too big, it might fall into the water. This is not a problem for the bulldog bat. It can take flight directly from the water!

Grade 6 Screening Test (continued)

13. A bat uses echolocation
    A. to see clearly at night.
    B. to hear where things are.
    C. to improve its sense of smell.
    D. to attract its prey.

14. In the second paragraph, what is the meaning of the phrase "periodically 'chirp' or 'screech' "?
    A. to pretend that it is a bird
    B. to flap its wings to create waves
    C. to stop flying and hold perfectly still
    D. to make noise from time to time

15. What does the bulldog bat do after it has caught a fish?
    A. It stores the fish and hunts for another.
    B. It drops into the water to eat the fish.
    C. It makes a loud "chirping" sound.
    D. It carries the fish away in its feet.

16. How did the bulldog bat get its name?
    A. It has the personality of a bulldog.
    B. It has a face that resembles a bulldog's.
    C. It has the same diet as a bulldog.
    D. It has a furry body like a bulldog.

17. In the third paragraph, "favorite cafeterias" refers to
    A. the bat's habitat.
    B. the bat's hunting methods.
    C. the bat's diet.
    D. the bat's hunting grounds.

18. What seems to be the author's attitude toward bats?
    A. fear
    B. interest
    C. awe
    D. indifference

19. Which of these best describes the passage?
    A. It lists characteristics of different bats.
    B. It describes a bat's different senses.
    C. It tells details about a certain type of bat.
    D. It explains why bats are not to be feared.

20. What is the passage mostly about?
    A. an unusual bat and its hunting method
    B. insect-eating bats versus fish-eating bats
    C. how certain bats get their names
    D. how bats are like birds

Grade 7 Screening Test

Directions: *Read each passage and answer the questions that follow it. Mark the letter of the best answer to each question.*

Wrapped in a new alpaca poncho, Sebastian continued his climb uphill. "How did the Incas do this?" he wondered to himself as he panted in the thin air. Sebastian himself was an American, but his parents were Peruvian, of Incan descent. From his parents, Sebastian had learned that the Incas had once ruled all of Peru and much of the Andes mountain range.

Much to his relief, Sebastian finally reached his destination: Machu Picchu. Machu Picchu is the site of an ancient Incan city. Its stone walls stretch across a mountaintop plateau.

The walls of Machu Picchu enfolded Sebastian in welcoming arms. For hours, he wandered among the ancient stones. With his attention focused on the ruins, Sebastian could easily forget the noisy tourists. In their place, he populated the city with Incan priestesses, colorfully dressed nobles, and swiftly running couriers.

As Sebastian left Machu Picchu, he ignored the vendors hawking cheap souvenirs. He wanted desperately to bring home something real and wonderful from his visit. Still, he knew it would be wrong to take even a small stone from the edge of one of the walls. Sebastian stared around the ancient ruins one last time and then grinned. He didn't need a souvenir of any kind; he has his memories of the visit. He would never forget his trip to Machu Picchu.

---

1. In the third paragraph, the description of the walls as "welcoming arms" helps emphasize
   A. the size and age of the city's walls.
   B. Sebastian's sense of belonging in the city of his ancestors.
   C. the cheerful hospitality of Machu Picchu's residents.
   D. the difficulty of the climb up to the city.

2. What does Sebastian imagine about Machu Picchu?
   A. It was the capital of the Incan empire.
   B. He helped to build the walls.
   C. He will live there someday.
   D. It is alive with ancient Incas.

3. How does Sebastian feel about Machu Picchu?
   A. He is amused by it.
   B. He is let down by it.
   C. He is impressed by it.
   D. He feels responsible for it.

4. What does Sebastian take with him from Machu Picchu?
   A. his memories
   B. some cheap souvenirs
   C. several pictures of the ruins
   D. a small rock from one of the walls

Grade 7 Screening Test (continued)

I treasured my visits to Grandpa Adair's and tried desperately to make them last. I spoke slowly, took tiny bites at mealtime, and stayed up late sipping hot lemon tea. Still, the days would sweep past like the summer wind, and soon I would find myself on the train home, clutching something old and precious from Grandpa Adair's attic.

Each time I visited Grandpa Adair I felt like I was collecting the pieces to a puzzle. Everything in his house was a part of his or Grandma's past, and everything had a story. It felt like it was my job to understand it all.

Grandpa and Grandma Adair had married young. I knew this from the photo on Grandpa's nightstand. Grandma looked no taller than I, but Grandpa said she was 18. "You're the spittin' image of her," he'd tell me, chuckling. "You've got her speckled green eyes." I studied the photo and memorized it. I knew every detail—the roses in her bouquet, the tufted white silk gown, her pointed satin slippers—by heart.

"Where's Grandma's wedding dress?" I asked one day.

"Oh," sighed Grandpa, "probably up in the attic being devoured by moths."

My heart leapt into my throat. Grandma's wedding gown—being devoured by moths? At that moment any attempts to slow down my visit and make each moment last were thrown out the window. There was no time to waste.

Everything in the attic was gray with dust, and sheets of lacy cobwebs stretched delicately from box to box. I ran a finger across the top of a steamer trunk as if to guess how many years had passed since other hands had touched it.

Breathing heavily, Grandpa turned over an empty fruit crate and sat down. "If your grandmother's dress is still up here, it's in that trunk," he said.

With a little effort, I released the front latch and lifted the lid. A cloud of dust swelled before me, and I waved my arms to clear the air. There, at the bottom of the trunk, was a pair of shoes. I reached down and extracted them gingerly. They were exquisite and tiny—the very satin slippers from the photo.

We found no dress—its whereabouts would remain a mystery—but the trip to the attic had not been a loss. I had Grandma's dainty white wedding shoes, and that part of the past would be safe with me.

Grade 7 Screening Test (continued)

5. What does the girl say about visits to her Grandpa?
   A. They are long and dull.
   B. They pass much too quickly.
   C. They happen once a year.
   D. They are quiet and still.

6. To the girl, what does Grandpa's house most resemble?
   A. a castle
   B. a log cabin
   C. a museum
   D. a skyscraper

7. How does the girl know that her grandparents married young?
   A. Grandpa told her the story of the wedding.
   B. She saw the picture on Grandpa's nightstand.
   C. She found the wedding certificate in the attic.
   D. She looked at the wedding photos in an album in the closet.

8. To what does the girl compare her visits to Grandpa's house?
   A. taking the train ride home
   B. reading an adventure novel
   C. walking on a stormy coast
   D. collecting pieces of a puzzle

9. The line "My heart leapt into my throat" helps to emphasize
   A. the girl's fondness of her grandpa.
   B. the strange noise coming out of the girl's mouth.
   C. the girl's excitement about exploring the attic.
   D. the girl's horror about the state of her grandma's dress.

10. Why does the girl run her finger across the old trunk?
   A. to leave a mark proving she had been in the attic
   B. to clear away some of the dust that had accumulated
   C. to express wonder at how long it had been untouched
   D. to see if it was as smooth as she remembered it to be

11. Where is Grandma's wedding dress?
   A. no one knows
   B. in the attic
   C. at the girl's house
   D. with Grandma

12. How does the girl feel about her grandparents' past?
   A. proud
   B. surprised
   C. fascinated
   D. worried

Grade 7 Screening Test *(continued)*

The ocean is home to many strange animals. Swimming birds and bears, mammals that look like fish, and fish that look like aliens are just a few of the unusual inhabitants. One more creature that should be included in this group is the marine iguana.

The marine iguana is the world's only sea-going lizard. It is native to the Galápagos Islands of Ecuador, where many other rare animals live. Marine iguanas can be four feet long, but at least half of that length comes from their tails. Although they look frightening, other animals have nothing to fear from marine iguanas. These wonderful sea-going lizards are herbivores, feeding almost exclusively on algae.

In order to eat algae, the iguanas dive into the ocean. Their dives usually last 5 to 10 minutes. Sometimes the iguanas' dives last for almost an hour even though they can't breathe underwater.

The water around the Galápagos is cold, and the iguanas are cold-blooded. When the iguanas get cold, they become sluggish. To raise their body temperature, iguanas bask in the sun.

Marine iguanas can be several different colors, from green to red to gray. They always wear a blotchy white mask. This speckling is not the iguanas' natural coloring; it's a crusted layer of salt. In order to keep their bodies free of salt even though they swim in salt water, marine iguanas "sneeze" salt.

Because they evolved without many predators, iguanas have little fear of other animals, including humans. Although this helps researchers observe them, it makes them easy prey for wild cats and other non-native animals that have been abandoned to their own pursuits on the islands. Although the marine iguana population has fallen, with help from governments and environmental organizations, these unusual animals are winning their fight to survive.

Grade 7 Screening Test (continued)

13. When would a marine iguana *most likely* need to bask in the sun?
    A. after escaping a wild cat
    B. after feeding on algae
    C. after lying on warm rocks
    D. after being weighed by a scientist

14. How do marine iguanas stay underwater to feed?
    A. They hold their breath.
    B. They use gills to breathe underwater.
    C. They are cold-blooded and don't have to breathe.
    D. They swallow bubbles of air that are trapped underwater.

15. In the fifth paragraph, the iguana's "mask" refers to
    A. the color of its skin.
    B. its coating of salt.
    C. the spines on its neck.
    D. its protective disguise.

16. In the last paragraph, what is the meaning of the phrase "abandoned to their own pursuits"?
    A. set free
    B. made into pets
    C. turned into marine animals
    D. trained to catch iguanas

17. How would a marine iguana probably respond to a tourist's presence?
    A. by crawling into the ocean
    B. by remaining underwater for an hour
    C. by repeatedly sneezing salt
    D. by ignoring the tourist completely

18. What seems to be the author's attitude toward marine iguanas?
    A. fear
    B. jealousy
    C. admiration
    D. pride

19. How has this passage been developed?
    A. It presents a general description of marine iguanas.
    B. It explains why the marine iguana population is declining.
    C. It describes how marine iguanas stay warm.
    D. It tells about the author's personal observation of marine iguanas.

20. What is this passage mostly about?
    A. How marine iguanas survive in cold water.
    B. The way marine iguanas choose their mates.
    C. Interesting details about marine iguanas.
    D. Marine iguanas' interaction with other animals.

Screening Tests
Answer Key

Grade 6 Screening Test

1. C
2. B
3. D
4. A
5. D
6. C
7. A
8. D
9. C
10. B
11. B
12. D
13. B
14. D
15. A
16. B
17. D
18. B
19. C
20. A

Grade 7 Screening Test

1. B
2. D
3. C
4. A
5. B
6. C
7. B
8. D
9. D
10. C
11. A
12. C
13. B
14. A
15. B
16. A
17. D
18. C
19. A
20. C

Name _____ Class _____ Date_____

Test 1—Grade 6 Geographic Literacy

Directions: *Use the map below to answer questions 1–3.*

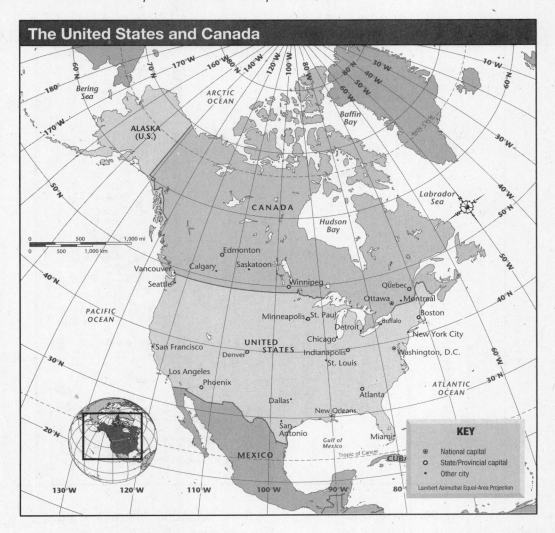

The United States and Canada

1. At what latitude and longitude is the city of New Orleans located?
   A. 40°N, 100°W
   B. 40°N, 80°W
   C. 30°N, 90°W
   D. 30°N, 100°W

2. Which of the following statements *best* describes the relative location of New Orleans?
   A. It is southwest of Atlanta.
   B. It is north of Denver.
   C. It is southwest of Dallas.
   D. It is northeast of Washington, D.C.

3. Which of the following statements *best* describes the approximate distance between Chicago and Washington, D.C.?
   A. The distance is approximately 2,000 kilometers.
   B. The distance is approximately 1,000 kilometers.
   C. The distance is approximately 50 kilometers.
   D. The distance is just over 150 kilometers.

Test 1—Grade 6 Geographic Literacy (continued)

Directions: *Use the map below to answer questions 4–7.*

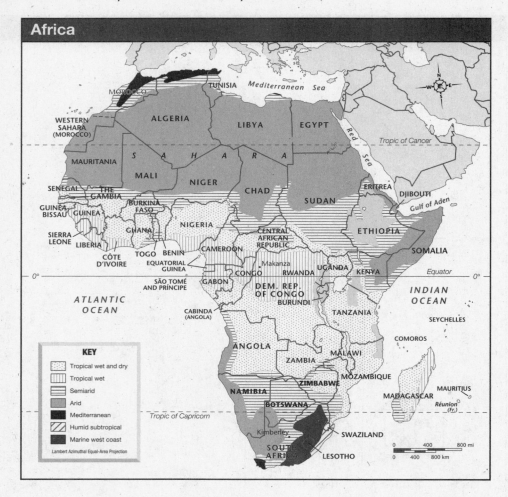

Africa

KEY
- Tropical wet and dry
- Tropical wet
- Semiarid
- Arid
- Mediterranean
- Humid subtropical
- Marine west coast

Lambert Azimuthal Equal-Area Projection

4. What two climate zones appear *most widely* throughout northern Africa?
   A. tropical wet and tropical wet and dry
   B. tropical wet and arid
   C. arid and semiarid
   D. semiarid and Mediterranean

5. According to the map, which of the following statements is true about Botswana?
   A. The Tropic of Capricorn passes through it.
   B. Most of the region has an arid climate.
   C. It is located west of South Africa.
   D. It has a tropical dry climate.

6. Arid land in Africa is usually bordered by
   A. humid subtropical regions.
   B. marine west coast regions.
   C. semiarid regions.
   D. tropical wet regions.

7. Which of the following cross the continent of Africa?
   1. Equator
   2. Tropic of Cancer
   3. Tropic of Capricorn
   A. 1 and 2 only   C. 1 and 3 only
   B. 1, 2, and 3   D. 2 and 3 only

Test 1—Grade 6 Geographic Literacy (continued)

Directions: *Use the map below to answer questions 8–11.*

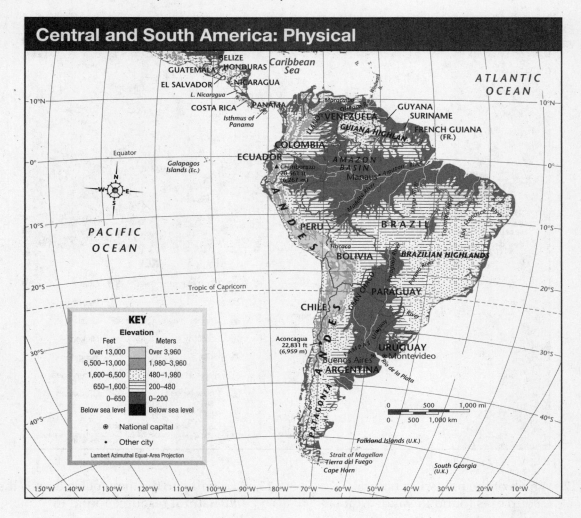

Central and South America: Physical

8. What type of information is shown in the key for the map of Central and South America?
   A. natural vegetation, mountain ranges, and physical features
   B. climatic regions, mountain ranges, and volcanoes
   C. elevation, national capitals, and other cities
   D. population density, wind currents, and geologic features

9. In which country is 10°S, 50°W located?
   A. Brazil   C. Peru
   B. Paraguay   D. Argentina

10. According to the map, which of the following areas has the *highest* elevation?
    A. the Brazilian Highlands
    B. the Andes Mountains
    C. the Guiana Highlands
    D. Patagonia

11. Which of the following bodies of water is located east of the Caribbean Sea?
    A. the Atlantic Ocean
    B. the Gulf of Mexico
    C. the Panama Canal
    D. the Pacific Ocean

Name _____ Class _____ Date_____

Test 1—Grade 6 Geographic Literacy (continued)

Directions: *Use the map below to answer questions 12–16.*

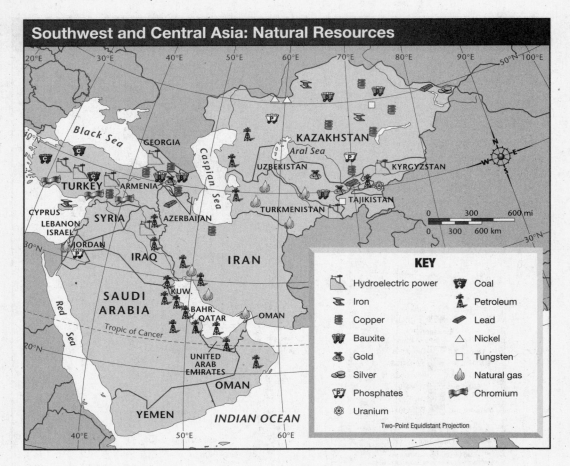

Southwest and Central Asia: Natural Resources

12. Which of the following natural resources is found in Saudi Arabia?
   A. silver   C. petroleum
   B. coal   D. iron

13. What natural resource is located immediately east of the Caspian Sea?
   A. bauxite   C. petroleum
   B. nickel   D. coal

14. Where are *most* of the petroleum resources located in Iran and Saudi Arabia?
   A. on their eastern borders
   B. near the coast
   C. on the Indian Ocean
   D. near their border with Kyrgyzstan

15. According to the map, petroleum is the *only* natural resource found in
   A. Oman.   C. Turkey.
   B. Iran.   D. Iraq.

16. Which of the following statements *best* describes the location of iron deposits nearest to the Aral Sea?
   A. Iron deposits are found northwest of the Aral Sea.
   B. Iron deposits are found east of the Aral Sea.
   C. Iron deposits are found northeast of the Aral Sea.
   D. Iron deposits are found southeast of the Aral Sea.

Test 2—Grade 7 Geographic Literacy

Directions: *Use the diagram below to answer questions 1–4.*

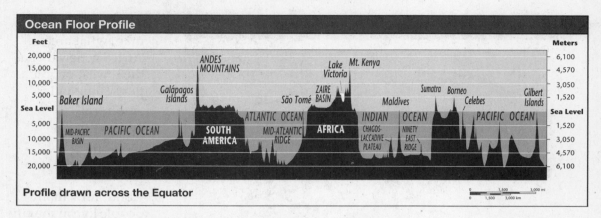

1. **What area of the world is shown on this map?**
   A. the ocean floor below South America and Africa
   B. the ocean floor below all of Earth
   C. the ocean floor along the Equator
   D. the ocean floor along the eastern hemisphere of Earth

2. **According to this diagram, what do Baker Island, the Galápagos Islands, and the Maldives have in common?**
   A. They are below sea level.
   B. They are at sea level.
   C. They are in the Pacific Ocean.
   D. They are surrounded by land.

3. **On this profile of the ocean floor, where are the lowest points on the Earth located?**
   A. in the Pacific Ocean
   B. in the Indian Ocean
   C. on the coast of South America
   D. in the Atlantic Ocean

4. **Based on the information in the diagram, which of the following is a true statement?**
   A. Mt. Kenya is the highest point on the South American continent.
   B. Celebes and Borneo are higher than Sumatra.
   C. Most of South America is at or near sea level, and most of Africa is above sea level.
   D. Lake Victoria is located at sea level.

Test 2—Grade 7 Geographic Literacy (continued)

Directions: *Use the map below to answer questions 5–9.*

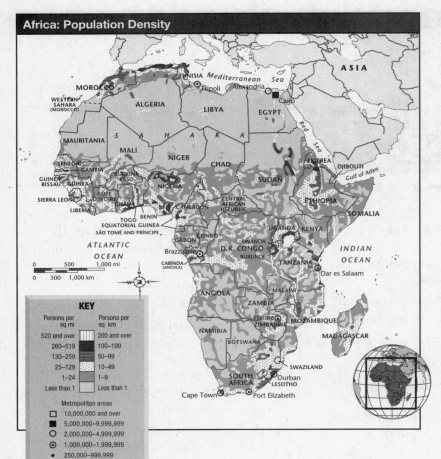

Africa: Population Density

5. According to this map, what area of Africa generally has the fewest people per square mile?
   A. central
   B. north
   C. south
   D. southwest

6. About how many people live in the city of Cairo, Egypt?
   A. between 2,000,000 and 4,999,999
   B. less than 1 person per square mile
   C. between 5,000,000 and 9,999,999
   D. 10,000,000 or more

7. What is the approximate distance between Cape Town, South Africa, and Harare, Zimbabwe?
   A. about 1,400 miles
   B. about 1,000 miles
   C. about 1,200 miles
   D. about 2,000 miles

8. Which of the following cities has the highest population?
   A. Tripoli, Libya
   B. Alexandria, Egypt
   C. Cairo, Egypt
   D. Dar es Salaam, Tanzania

9. Using this map, what is the one thing the South African cities of Cape Town, Port Elizabeth, and Durban have in common?
   A. They are in areas with 10 to 49 people per square mile.
   B. They are located on Africa's western coast.
   C. They are located on Africa's southern coast.
   D. Their populations are 10,000,000 and over.

Test 2—Grade 7 Geographic Literacy (continued)

Directions: *Use the map below to answer questions 10–13.*

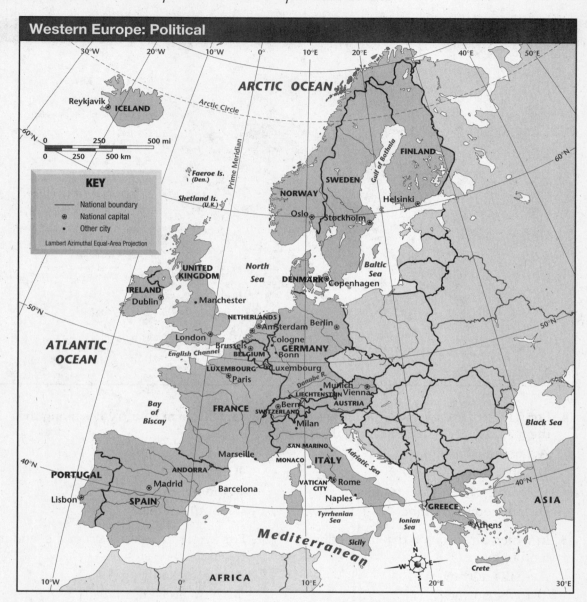

Western Europe: Political

10. What is the capital city of Italy?
   A. Rome   C. Naples
   B. Milan   D. Paris

11. Which of the following cities is the closest in distance to Vienna, Austria?
   A. Lisbon   C. Athens
   B. Helsinki   D. Dublin

12. Which country is located west of Spain?
   A. Portugal   C. Finland
   B. United Kingdom   D. Italy

13. Which body of water separates the United Kingdom and France?
   A. Bay of Biscay
   B. English Channel
   C. North Sea
   D. Mediterranean Sea

Name _____ Class _____ Date_____

Test 2—Grade 7 Geographic Literacy (continued)

Directions: *Use the map below to answer questions 14–17.*

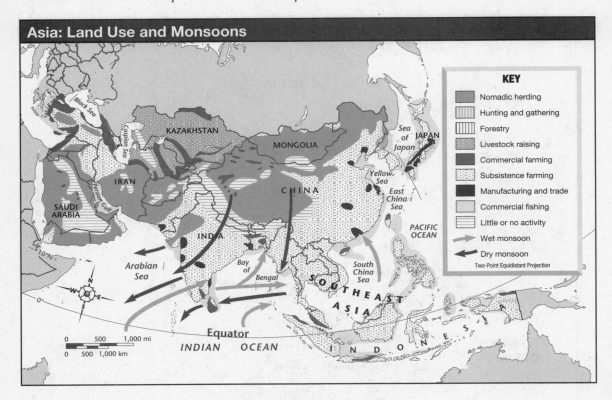

14. For which of the following activities is the majority of the land in India used?
  A. nomadic herding
  B. subsistence farming
  C. manufacturing and trade
  D. commercial farming

15. In which direction do dry monsoons tend to move?
  A. to the northwest
  B. to the northeast
  C. to the southeast
  D. to the southwest

16. Which Asian country lies along the equator?
  A. China
  B. India
  C. Indonesia
  D. Saudi Arabia

17. For what purpose is *most* of the land in Kazakhstan used?
  A. livestock raising
  B. commercial farming
  C. subsistence farming
  D. commercial fishing

Name _____ Class _____ Date_____

Test 3—Grade 6 Visual Analysis

Directions: *Study the diagram of sections and township. Then answer questions 1–4.*

The Land Ordinance of 1785 set up a system for surveying and settling the Northwest Territory. The Land Ordinance of 1785 divided the land into townships that consist of 36 sections.

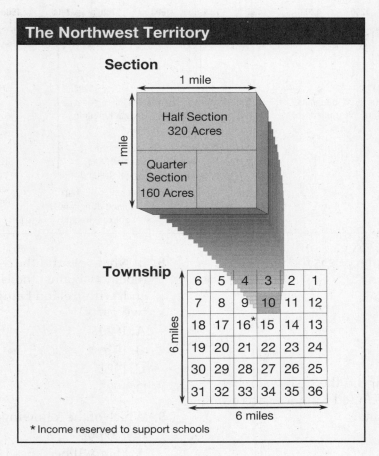

1. According to the diagram, how many square miles are in each section?
   A. 6 square miles
   B. 1 square mile
   C. 36 square miles
   D. 1/4 square mile

2. How many acres are in each half section?
   A. 320 acres
   B. 160 acres
   C. 1 acre
   D. 36 acres

3. How many square miles are in each township?
   A. 6 square miles
   B. 12 square miles
   C. 36 square miles
   D. 360 square miles

4. How many sections in a township are reserved to support schools?
   A. 10 sections
   B. 6 sections
   C. 2 sections
   D. 1 section

Name _____ Class _____ Date_____

Test 3—Grade 6 Visual Analysis (continued)

Directions: *Use the timeline below to answer questions 5–9.*

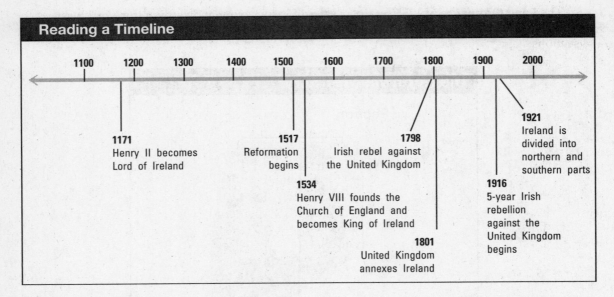

Reading a Timeline

1100 1200 1300 1400 1500 1600 1700 1800 1900 2000

1171
Henry II becomes
Lord of Ireland

1517
Reformation
begins

1798
Irish rebel against
the United Kingdom

1921
Ireland is
divided into
northern and
southern parts

1534
Henry VIII founds the
Church of England and
becomes King of Ireland

1916
5-year Irish
rebellion
against the
United Kingdom
begins

1801
United Kingdom
annexes Ireland

5. Into what intervals is the timeline divided?
   A. 1,000 years
   B. 100 years
   C. 500 years
   D. 50 years

6. In what year did the Irish *first* rebel against the United Kingdom according to the timeline?
   A. 1517
   B. 1798
   C. 1800
   D. 1921

7. Which of the following events occurred *before* the founding of the Church of England by Henry VIII?
   A. Ireland is divided into northern and southern parts.
   B. United Kingdom annexes Ireland.
   C. Henry VIII becomes King of Ireland.
   D. Henry II becomes Lord of Ireland.

8. In what year did the 5-year Irish rebellion against the United Kingdom end, with Ireland being divided into two parts?
   A. 1900
   B. 1916
   C. 1921
   D. 1925

9. Which of the following events occurred *after* 1700?
   A. Henry II becomes Lord of Ireland.
   B. The Reformation begins.
   C. Henry VIII founds the Church of England.
   D. United Kingdom annexes Ireland.

Name _____ Class _____ Date_____

Test 4—Grade 7 Visual Analysis

Directions: *Use the timeline below to answer questions 1–5.*

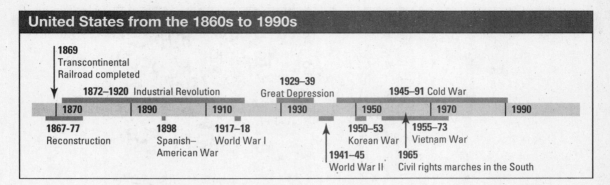

United States from the 1860s to 1990s

1869
Transcontinental
Railroad completed

1872–1920 Industrial Revolution

1929–39
Great Depression

1945–91 Cold War

1870   1890   1910   1930   1950   1970   1990

1867-77
Reconstruction

1898
Spanish–
American War

1917–18
World War I

1950–53
Korean War

1955–73
Vietnam War

1941–45
World War II

1965
Civil rights marches in the South

1. According to the timeline, which sequence of events is correct?
   A. Spanish-American War; Industrial Revolution; World War II; Great Depression
   B. Reconstruction; Great Depression; Korean War; Vietnam War
   C. Great Depression; World War I; Cold War; Industrial Revolution
   D. World War I; World War II; Great Depression; Korean War

2. Which of the following statements is true, based on the information from the timeline?
   A. Between 1910 and 1970, the United States experienced six wars.
   B. The end of the Great Depression was marked by the beginning of World War I.
   C. At the end of World War I, the Industrial Revolution nearly ended.
   D. The Korean War and the Vietnam War overlapped by two years.

3. Which of the following events occurred during the Cold War?
   A. World War II
   B. the Great Depression
   C. the Vietnam War
   D. the Industrial Revolution

4. During which of the following periods did civil rights marches in the South occur?
   A. Reconstruction
   B. World War I
   C. the Great Depression
   D. the Cold War

5. Which event on the timeline spans the greatest amount of time?
   A. the Great Depression
   B. Transcontinental Railroad completed
   C. Industrial Revolution
   D. Korean War

Name _____ Class _____ Date_____

Test 4—Grade 7 Visual Analysis *(continued)*

Directions: *Examine the cartoon below, and answer questions 6–10.*

6. Who or what do the people in the water represent?
   A. They represent people who have jumped in before knowing how to swim.
   B. They represent Russians trying to invade the U.S. shorelines.
   C. They represent immigrants coming to the United States.
   D. They represent big business in America.

7. Who or what does the lifeguard represent?
   A. He represents the European Union.
   B. He represents the United States Coast Guard.
   C. He represents American immigrants.
   D. He represents the United States government.

8. Which of the following would be the *best* caption for the cartoon?
   A. "Who taught these people how to speak English?"
   B. "Uncle Sam realizes he can't swim."
   C. "Can America save everyone?"
   D. "The war against terrorism comes to America's shores."

9. Which of the following scenes presents the message *most* similar to the one displayed in the cartoon?
   A. A woman dressed as the Statue of Liberty looks sadly at a long line of children carrying empty bowls as she ladles the last of her pot of oatmeal to the first child in line.
   B. The President of the United States shakes hands with the president of another nation.
   C. An older man and woman sit on a park bench smiling and laughing as they toss bread to a flock of hungry pigeons.
   D. A well-dressed man and woman look away as they walk past a long line of homeless people begging for money.

10. Which of the following statements *best* explains the symbolism in this cartoon?
    A. The umbrella is a symbol that represents the sky.
    B. The chair is a symbol that represents big business.
    C. The world "Help" is a symbol that represents English-speaking immigrants.
    D. The life preserver is a symbol that represents American aid.

Test 5—Grade 6 Critical Thinking and Reading

Directions: *Read the following passage. Then answer questions 1–4.*

"From this the question arises whether it is better to be loved more than feared, or feared more than loved. The reply is, that one ought to be both feared and loved, but as it is difficult for the two to go together, it is much safer to be feared than loved…for it may be said of men in general that they are ungrateful,…anxious to avoid danger, and greedy…. Men find it easier to attack one who makes himself loved than one who makes himself feared…

A prince…must imitate the fox and the lion, for the lion cannot protect himself from traps, and the fox cannot defend himself from wolves. One must therefore be a fox to recognize traps, and a lion to frighten wolves…. Therefore, a wise ruler ought not keep his word when doing so would be against his interest…. If men were all good, this [rule] would not be a good one; but as they are bad, and would not be honest with you, so you are not bound to keep your word with them…."

—Niccoló Machiavelli, *The Prince* (1513)

1. Which of the following does Machiavelli contrast in this passage?
   A. a fox and a lion
   B. a fox and a wolf
   C. a wolf and a lion
   D. a lion and a wise ruler

2. Machiavelli would *most likely* disagree with which of the following statements?
   A. Men are mostly bad.
   B. A prince is responsible for keeping his word.
   C. A prince cannot survive without both intelligence and strength.
   D. A feared ruler is a powerful ruler.

3. To which category do the following belong?
   - Men are greedy.
   - Men are ungrateful.
   - Men are anxious to avoid danger.
   A. reasons it is safer to be loved than feared
   B. reasons to imitate a lion
   C. reasons to imitate a wolf
   D. reasons it is safer to be feared than loved

4. Which of the following *best* describes a "Machiavellian" leader?
   A. one who rejects morality to pursue political gains
   B. one who guarantees that his or her subjects are fairly treated
   C. one who has feelings of inferiority
   D. one who expects all people to be fair and honest

Test 5—Grade 6 Critical Thinking and Reading (continued)

Directions: *Read the following passage. Then answer questions 5–7.*

> *The Sirens: A Greek Myth From the Adventures of Ulysses*, retold by Bernard Evslin
> "In the first light of the morning Ulysses awoke and called his crew about him.
> 'Men,' he said. 'Listen well, for your lives today hang upon what I am about to tell you. That large island to the west is Thrinacia, where we must make landfall, for our provisions run low. But to get to the island we must pass through a narrow strait. And at the head of the strait is a rocky islet where dwell two sisters called Sirens, whose voices you must not hear. Now I shall guard you against their singing, which would lure you to shipwreck, but first you must bind me to the mast. Tie me tightly, as though I were a dangerous captive. And no matter how I struggle, no matter what signals I make to you, do not release me, lest I follow their voices to destruction, taking you with me.'
> Thereupon Ulysses took a large lump of the beeswax…and kneaded it in his powerful hands until it became soft. Then he went to each man of the crew and plugged his ears with soft wax; he caulked their ears so tightly they could hear nothing but the thin pulsing of their own blood….
> Ulysses had left his own ears unplugged because he had to remain in command of the ship and had need of his hearing. Every sound means something upon the sea. But when they drew near the rocky islet and he heard the first faint strains of the Sirens' singing, then he wished he, too, had stopped his own ears with wax. All his strength suddenly surged toward the sound of those magical voices. The very hair of his head seemed to be tugging at his scalp, trying to fly away. His eyeballs started out of his head."

5. Put the following events in the sequence in which they would have occurred on Ulysses' ship.
   1. Tie Ulysses to the mast.
   2. Pass through a narrow strait.
   3. Reach Thrinacia.
   4. Put wax in your ears.

   A. 4, 1, 2, 3   **C.** 2, 1, 3, 4
   B. 4, 1, 3, 2   **D.** 1, 4, 2, 3

6. What would be the *most likely* effect if the crew released Ulysses?
   A. The Sirens would board the ship and take control.
   B. The Sirens would regain their status as captain of the ship.
   C. Ulysses and his crew would die because Ulysses would follow the Sirens' voices and lead the crew to shipwreck.
   D. Ulysses would drown before he had a chance to hear the Sirens sing.

7. From the information in the passage, what do you think was the fate of the other ships and crews who tried to reach the island?
   A. The ships were boarded by the Sirens, and the crews were taken prisoner.
   B. The ships turned around, and the crews returned home.
   C. The ships were captured by the Sirens, and the crews were drowned.
   D. The Sirens' voices lured the crews to steer toward the rocks, the ships were destroyed, and the crews were killed.

Test 5—Grade 6 Critical Thinking and Reading *(continued)*

Directions: *Read the following passage. Then answer questions 8 and 9.*

> In 1989, communism in Poland ended, and Poland adopted the free enterprise system. In this kind of system, people can open and run their own businesses free from government control. The fall of communism meant that the government no longer controlled the creation of jobs. As a result, many government jobs disappeared. The loss of jobs forced people to look for jobs elsewhere. Because of free enterprise, small companies now have the freedom to grow naturally. Growing companies have created new and better jobs for some people, but other people remain jobless.

8. What is the main idea of this passage?
   A. After communism, many government jobs in Poland were eliminated, but privately owned businesses created new, better jobs.
   B. When communism ended in Poland, government businesses thrived despite the elimination of many government jobs.
   C. After communism ended in Poland, people did not want government jobs any longer.
   D. Growing companies in Poland after communism made the country a global economic power.

9. Which of the following statements would *most likely* be supported by a member of the Communist party?
   A. Poland adopted the free enterprise system so that businesses would not be government-controlled.
   B. The free enterprise system created many new and better jobs.
   C. Many small companies were formed as a result of the free enterprise system.
   D. Poland's economy suffered when communism ended, and people lost their jobs.

Directions: *Read the following passage. Then answer questions 10 and 11.*

> "My friends…when you deposit money in a bank, the bank does not put the money in a safe deposit vault. It invests your money, puts it to work…. [Why did banks go out of business?] There was a general rush so great that the soundest banks could not get enough currency to meet demand…. [Then he described the plan to gradually reopen banks.] There is no occasion for worry…. When people find they can get their money, the phantom of fear will soon be laid [to rest]. I can assure you that it is safer to keep your money in a reopened bank than under the mattress."
> —President Franklin D. Roosevelt, in a radio "fireside chat" (1933)

10. Which of the following is an opinion?
    A. When people find they can get their money, the phantom of fear will soon be laid to rest.
    B. Banks could not get enough currency to meet people's demands.
    C. Some people kept their money under mattresses instead of in a bank.
    D. Banks invest deposited money.

11. With which of the following statements would a banker probably disagree?
    A. Banks are probably the safest place to keep money.
    B. Investing deposited money is an irresponsible function of a bank.
    C. The responsibility of a bank is to use deposited money wisely.
    D. People who deposit their money in a bank will not worry much.

Name _____ Class _____ Date_____

Test 5—Grade 6 Critical Thinking and Reading (continued)

Directions: *Read the following passage. Then answer questions 12–14.*

> "This is the country for a man to enjoy himself: Ohio, Indiana, and the Missouri Territory….
>
> There is enough to spare of everything a person can desire; [I] have not heard either man or woman speak a word against the government or the price of [food and other supplies].
>
> The poorest families adorn [decorate] the table three times a day like a wedding dinner…. Say, is it so in England?
>
> If you knew the difference between this country and England you would need no persuading to leave it and come hither [here]."
>
> —Samuel Crabtree, in a letter to his brother in England about what he found after arriving in the United States (1818)

12. Which of the following two things in America does Samuel Crabtree contrast with those in England?

    A. man or woman and the government

    B. people's opinions of the government and the resources available to them

    C. poor families and a wedding dinner

    D. the price of food and supplies

13. What is the purpose of Samuel Crabtree's letter?

    A. to plead with his brother to rescue him from the hardships of America

    B. to describe his unhappiness with life in America

    C. to persuade his brother to move to America

    D. to describe how the poorest families lived

14. How does Samuel Crabtree's letter show his pride in his country?

    A. He is proud that he does not have contact with England.

    B. He thinks people are unhappy with the price of food.

    C. He doesn't understand how the poor can eat three times a day.

    D. His letter shows the economic opportunity that Americans enjoyed.

Directions: *Read the following passage. Then answer question 15.*

> Officials of a major city in the United States are developing plans to build a new mass transit system that would replace the current outdated system. The officials are concerned with correcting several major problems that exist in the current system such as, increasing the number of passengers the system can accommodate and decreasing long delays during peak traffic times. Also, the current route does not travel to areas of new business development in the downtown area, its tracks have caused a major highway to be redirected, and the system has been known to malfunction during the city's harsh winters.

15. Which of the following would *not* address a concern of the officials as they work to develop a new mass transit system?

    A. updating the location of stations throughout the city

    B. providing additional seating capacity

    C. designing new routes that allow traffic to pass more freely

    D. installing automated ticket machines at each station

Test 5—Grade 6 Critical Thinking and Reading (continued)

Directions: *Read the following passage. Then answer questions 16–18.*

> "With this lodging and diet, our extreme [work] in bearing and planting [stockade walls]…strained and bruised us, and our continual labor in the [extreme] heat…weakened us….
>
> From May to September, [we]…lived upon [fish], and sea crabs. Fifty in this time we buried….
>
> But now all our [food was gone], the [fish] gone, all helps abandoned, [and] each hour [we expected] the fury of the [natives]….God, the patron of all good [efforts]…so changed the hearts of the [natives] that they brought such plenty of their fruits and provisions as no man wanted."
>
> —John Smith, describing the "starving time" of Jamestown colony in 1607, from the *General History of Virginia* (1624)

16. You are one of the Jamestown colonists who was starving in 1607, and the Indians have not brought food for you to eat. You attend a colony meeting. Which of the following suggestions would you reject as you work to find a solution to your hunger?
    A. Some of the men should leave the colony to find food.
    B. The colony should work toward peaceful relations with the Indians and ask them to teach the colonists how to survive.
    C. The colonists should barter with the Indians for food.
    D. The colonists should wait for supplies from England.

17. To what was John Smith referring when he wrote "Fifty in this time we buried…"?
    A. colonists
    B. Native Americans
    C. fish
    D. crabs

18. Which of the following *best* explains why John Smith attributes the Indians' good will toward the colonists to God?
    A. The Indians did not want to fight with the colonists anymore.
    B. The colonists believed that God had abandoned them.
    C. God helped the Indians see that the colonists needed help as a reward to the colonists for their hard work.
    D. Some colonists were unhappy that their survival was a result of the Indians' help.

Test 5—Grade 6 Critical Thinking and Reading (continued)

Directions: *Read the following passage. Then answer question 19.*

> "The first reason why we [left] Russia, it is because we would like to have freedom....
> I have freedom here. I can see here not propaganda movies, not propaganda plays, not propaganda literature. I can talk with different people. If I want, I can move [to] another city, [to] another country. Maybe I [won't] go to another country, but I know absolutely exactly that [it] is possible."
> —Yuri Sinelnikov, describing why he and his wife left the Soviet Union to come to the United States, in an interview (1970s)

19. Which of the following *best* describes the viewpoint of Yuri Sinelnikov toward America?
    A. He understands that he can move to another country.
    B. He recognizes and appreciates the freedoms of the United States.
    C. He is bitter toward Russia because of the propaganda that he was forced to watch and read while he lived there.
    D. He values the propaganda that he read and watched while living in Russia.

Directions: *Read the following passage. Then answer question 20.*

> **A Cherokee woman, urging resistance to the United States government plan to move their people west, in a petition (1818):**
> "We have heard with painful feelings that the bounds of the land we now possess are to be drawn into very narrow limits. The land was given to us by the Great Spirit above as our common right, to raise our children upon.... We, therefore, humbly petition...the head men of warriors, to hold out to the last in support of our common rights, as the Cherokee nations have been the first settlers of the land....[We] claim the right of the soil."
> **John Louis O'Sullivan, describing the nation's destiny to grow, in an editorial in the New York Morning News (1845):**
> "Our manifest destiny [is] to overspread and to possess the whole of the continent which [God] has given us for the development of the great experiment of liberty and federated self-government entrusted to us."

20. Which of the following statements *best* summarizes the views of the writers above?
    A. Each writer claims that lands in North America have been granted to a certain group of people by a divine power.
    B. Each writer argues for the right of Native Americans to remain on the lands where they currently lived.
    C. Each writer supports the right of the United States government to expand its authority across the North American continent.
    D. Each writer believes that Native Americans and the United States government will compromise over land ownership issues.

Test 6—Grade 7 Critical Thinking and Reading

Directions: *Read the following passage. Then answer questions 1–4.*

At the battle of Gettysburg in July 1863, both the North and the South suffered heavy casualties. On November 19, 1863, President Abraham Lincoln visited Gettysburg to dedicate the battlefield cemetery, and delivered the following speech.

The Gettysburg Address

Four score and seven years ago our fathers brought forth on this continent, a new nation, conceived in liberty, and dedicated to the proposition that all men are created equal.

Now we are engaged in a great civil war, testing whether that nation, or any nation, so conceived and so dedicated, can long endure. We are met on a great battlefield of that war. We have come to dedicate a portion of that field, as a final resting place for those who here gave their lives that that nation might live. It is altogether fitting and proper that we should do this. But in a larger sense, we cannot dedicate—we cannot consecrate—we cannot hallow—this ground. The brave men, living and dead, who struggled here have consecrated it, far above our poor power to add or detract. The world will little note, nor long remember what we say here, but it can never forget what they did here. It is for us the living, rather, to be dedicated here to the unfinished work which they who fought here have thus far so nobly advanced. It is rather for us to be here dedicated to the great task remaining before us—that from these honored dead we take increased devotion to that cause for which they gave the last full measure of devotion—that we here highly resolve that these dead shall not have died in vain—that this nation, under God, shall have a new birth of freedom—and that government of the people, by the people, for the people shall not perish from the earth.

---

1. What does President Lincoln say is the *best* way to honor the soldiers who have died at the Battle of Gettysburg?

   A. Attack the enemy forces on the great battlefield of Gettysburg.

   B. Keep the principles of democracy that they died for alive.

   C. Seek immediate revenge on those who would threaten democracy.

   D. Refuse to be drawn into another meaningless war.

2. What is the "unfinished work" that President Lincoln believes the American people still have to do?

   A. They need to ensure that the principles of our nation do not fail.

   B. They need to consecrate the soldiers who have fought in all wars.

   C. They need to continue to expand America's borders.

   D. The need to ensure that foreign nations do not destroy the Union.

3. What is the *most likely* effect of President Lincoln's speech?

   A. Listeners will be discouraged from supporting the war effort.

   B. The government of the United States will be dissolved.

   C. Congress will withdraw support for a memorial at Gettysburg.

   D. Listeners will have greater dedication for Lincoln's cause.

4. What might have been one reason that President Lincoln chose to give a speech about the future of the nation when dedicating the cemetery?

   A. to consecrate the ground in memory of the dead soldiers

   B. to emphasize that no one died in vain, and that we must continue their fight

   C. to encourage young men to fight for freedom by enlisting

   D. to cause families to fear that their sons might perish in the war

Test 6—Grade 7 Critical Thinking and Reading (continued)

Directions: *Read the story* "The Envious Buffalo" *from* The Fables of India, *retold by Joseph Gaer. Then answer questions 5–8.*

On a small farm in southern India there lived a water buffalo named Big Red Bubalus with his younger brother named Little Red Bubalus. These two brothers did all the hard work on the farm. They plowed and they harrowed; they seeded; and they brought in the harvest for their owner.

Yet for all their labors they were rarely rewarded. And all they were given to eat was grass and straw, or chaff when the grain was husked.

This same farmer owned a pig who did nothing but eat and wallow in the water pumped up for him by the buffaloes. Yet the hog was fed on rice and millet and was well taken care of by the farmer and his family.

Little Red Bubalus complained to his brother: "We, who do all the hard work, are treated shabbily and our master gives us next to nothing to eat. Most of the time we have to go out into the pasture to find our own food. Yet this lazy pig is fed all the time and never does any work."

"Envy him not, little brother," said Big Red Bubalus….

One day the farmer's only daughter was engaged to be married. And as the wedding day drew near, the hog was slaughtered and roasted for the wedding feast.

Then Big Red Bubalus said to Little Red Bubalus: "Now do you see why a pig is not to be envied?"

And Little Red Bubalus replied: "Yes, now I understand. It is better to feed on straw and chaff, and to live out our lives, than to be fattened on rice only to end up on a roasting spit."

5. This story is a fable that teaches a lesson about life called a *moral*. What is the moral of this story?
   A. Do not waste time working when you can rest.
   B. Do not wish for what you can never have.
   C. We should not envy others but should appreciate the good in our own lives.
   D. Only buffaloes have to suffer.

6. What happens after Little Red Bubalus complains?
   A. Big Red Bubalus says nothing.
   B. Big Red Bubalus responds, "Envy him not, little brother."
   C. The pig is rewarded with rice and millet.
   D. Big Red Bubalus is punished.

7. Complete this word analogy of the pig : _____ :: the buffaloes : _____
   A. business people, rich people
   B. young people, old people
   C. leisurely people, hard-working people
   D. messy people, neat people

8. How does understanding the situation help Little Red Bubalus?
   A. It helps Little Red Bubalus understand that someday he will be like the pig.
   B. It helps Little Red Bubalus understand that Big Red Bubalus is wrong.
   C. It helps Little Red Bubalus understand that his work has reward.
   D. It helps Little Red Bubalus understand that now he will be fed millet.

Test 6—Grade 7 Critical Thinking and Reading *(continued)*

Directions: *Read the passage below that describes the Korean martial art of* tae kwon do. *Then answer questions 9–12.*

The martial arts are ways of fighting…but a person who [practices the martial arts] tries to act in ways that bring peace. [Those who practice the martial arts] do not fight in real life unless there is no other choice. Koreans developed the martial art of *tae kwon do* more than 2,000 years ago. Today, it is one of the most popular martial arts in the world.

The name *tae kwon do* means "the art of kicking and punching." Tae kwon do is especially famous for its jumping and spinning kicks… Students of tae kwon do combine quick, straight movements with circular, flowing movements.

To students of tae kwon do, their art is more than a way to defend themselves. It is a way of life. Students learn the following rules:

- be loyal to your country, your school, and your friends
- respect your family, your teachers, and your elders
- maintain a strong spirit and never give up
- finish what you begin

Tae kwon do students promise to follow these rules. They also vow to work hard and keep up with schoolwork. But most of all, they commit themselves to behaving in ways that are kind and peaceful.

---

9. Which of the following statements *best* characterizes tae kwon do?
   A. It is a martial art that teaches how to defend yourself without working on solutions with the enemy.
   B. It is a martial art that teaches people new ways to harm their enemies.
   C. It is a martial art that teaches students how to defend themselves and how to live peacefully.
   D. It is a martial art that involves no loyalty to any one nation or ruler.

10. Which of the following people is applying tae kwon do's lessons ?
   A. Despite getting low grades in his spelling test last week, Juan studied even harder the following week.
   B. Marguerite told her older brother that her middle school was the worst in the city.
   C. Aaron practiced his kicks all evening, even though he promised his mother he would spend the evening studying.
   D. Instead of finishing her homework, Rachel went to the pep rally to root for her friends on the football team.

11. If a person thought tae kwon do only involved fighting in a ring, how would that person be wrong?
   A. Tae kwon do is a way to defend oneself, but it is also a way of life.
   B. Tae kwon do students spend their time studying and thinking.
   C. Tae kwon do is a way of life, and those who practice it today never use it for fighting.
   D. Tae kwon do is not fought in a ring anymore, but fighters still do this if necessary.

12. How might tae kwon do help provide the discipline necessary for one to lead a successful life?
   A. Tae kwon do teaches students that physical strength is important.
   B. Tae kwon do improves one's intelligence.
   C. Tae kwon do forbids students from fighting
   D. Tae kwon do teaches students not to give up and always do their best.

Test 6—Grade 7 Critical Thinking and Reading (continued)

Directions: *The passage below is from Jennifer Seymour Whitaker's book,* How Can Africa Survive? *It describes the changes that European colonization brought to the traditional role of women in Africa. Read the passage below. Then answer questions 13–16.*

[T]he small farmers who represent most of Africa's populace are politically mute. And none more so than Africa's women farmers, who grow perhaps 70 percent of the continent's food....

In the pre-colonial era, both worked within the subsistence economy. Women farmed and did household chores, while men focused on hunting and war and helped with clearing land and harvesting...An African woman often lived a life quite separately economically from that of her husband, in which the basic unit was herself and her children.... Her husband most often provided her with a hut and some land to farm. She sustained her family by working the land allotted to her and by trading....

[H]owever, with the introduction of cash crops by the colonial administrators, the division of labor shifted further against women.... Regarding wives as homemakers and husbands as breadwinners, the Europeans either did not understand or refused to accept the fact that most African farming was done by women....

Twenty-five years of independence have done little to redress this balance. Because women are even poorer than their husbands and brothers, they are correspondingly less able to make the investments necessary to maintain or increase [crop] yields....

13. Which of the following statements *best* expresses Whitaker's viewpoint about the division of labor in Africa ?
   A. It has caused many wars.
   B. It changes with the seasons.
   C. It has hurt women.
   D. It has always been divided equally between men and women.

14. How was the division of labor in pre-colonial Africa different than that of present-day Africa?
   A. The division of labor was more equal in pre-colonial Africa, but it changed with the introduction of cash crops.
   B. The division of labor was different in pre-colonial Africa because men did all the household chores.
   C. The division of labor was different in pre-colonial Africa because women focused on hunting and war.
   D. The division of labor was different in pre-colonial Africa because women were regarded as breadwinners.

15. Which of the following solutions would Whitaker *most likely* support to improve the condition of women farmers in Africa?
   A. education and training to help women farmers learn farming techniques
   B. an increase in taxes on imported food and farming equipment
   C. loans to help women farmers buy better equipment and seed
   D. stricter marriage and divorce laws to prevent breakup of families

16. With which statement would Whitaker *most likely* disagree?
   A. European colonists introduced export crops that hurt the welfare of the continent of Africa as a whole.
   B. European colonists accepted the fact that most of the farming in Africa was done by women.
   C. European colonists helped create a situation in which women farmers in Africa can barely survive.
   D. European colonists set a standard in Africa that is harmful to women today.

Name _____ Class _____ Date_____

Test 7—Grade 6 Communications

Directions: *Read the following statements about Adolf Hitler, dictator of Germany from 1933 to 1945. Then answer questions 1–4.*

1. Adolf Hitler was born in Branau, Austria, in 1889.
2. While in jail after an unsuccessful attempt to overthrow the Bavarian government, Hitler wrote *Mein Kampf.*
3. *Mein Kampf* is one of the most influential political books ever written.
4. Hitler gave himself the title *Führer* ("Leader") in 1934.
5. Two of Hitler's foreign policy goals were the destruction of the Treaty of Versailles and the transformation of Germany into a military power in Europe.
6. If Hitler had not been so egotistical, he would have succeeded in his plans to dominate Europe.
7. Hitler was stubborn; he refused to leave his headquarters in Berlin, Germany, when the Soviets arrived in the city.
8. Hitler, the most brutal dictator the world has ever known, was responsible for the mass extermination of nearly 6 million Jews.

1. If you were giving a speech arguing that Hitler had several objectives after gaining power, which of the statements should you use as evidence.
   A. Statement 6
   B. Statement 5
   C. Statement 4
   D. Statement 8

2. Jacob has concluded that Hitler was a cruel leader. Which statement *best* supports Jacob's conclusion?
   A. Statement 5
   B. Statement 6
   C. Statement 7
   D. Statement 8

3. Which of the following people would be the *most* reliable source for Statement 7?
   A. a French soldier who fought in the war
   B. a German officer who was with Hitler that day
   C. an American reporter based in France
   D. an American citizen who worked in weapons factories during the war

4. Maria is writing a paragraph in her history class about the book *Mein Kampf.* Statement 2 is her first sentence. Statement 3 is her second sentence, and states the main idea of her paragraph. Which of the following statements would be the *most* effective third sentence?
   A. The title means "My Struggle," and the work is particularly interesting because it became the guidebook of Hitler's government.
   B. Hitler was hated by many people who feared his rapid rise to power.
   C. The book is boring because it discusses issues that affected Germany and Poland but not the United States.
   D. Had he left his headquarters in Berlin when the Soviets arrived, Hitler would have dominated most of Europe.

Test 7—Grade 6 Communications *(continued)*

Directions: *Read the passage below. Compare the passage with the information in the timeline. Then answer questions 5–8.*

> Some emperors made strong efforts to stop the steady decline of the Roman Empire. Although Diocletian persecuted Christians, he also worked to strengthen Rome. He enlarged the army and built new forts at the borders. He also improved the system of collecting taxes. This brought in more money to pay the army. Diocletian divided the empire into two parts to make it easier to rule. He ruled over the more wealthy east and appointed a co-emperor to rule over the west.

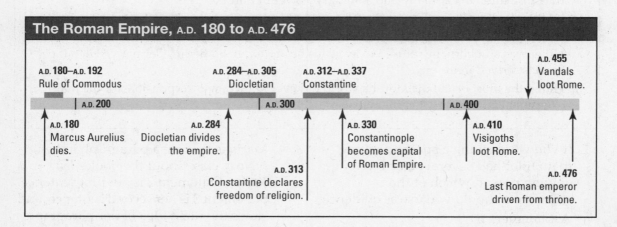

5. Which of the events on the timeline is the passage *most likely* describing?
   A. Marcus Aurelius dies.
   B. Diocletian divides the empire.
   C. Constantine declares freedom of religion.
   D. Constantinople becomes the capital of the Roman Empire.

6. When did the Visigoths loot Rome?
   A. A.D. 180   C. A.D. 410
   B. A.D. 330   D. A.D. 455

7. In A.D. 212, all free people in the Roman Empire were granted citizenship. Where on the timeline should this event be placed?
   A. between A.D. 313 and A.D. 330
   B. between A.D. 180 and A.D. 284
   C. between A.D. 410 and A.D. 455
   D. between A.D. 330 and A.D. 410

8. In what year did Diocletian divide the Roman Empire?
   A. A.D. 180   C. A.D. 305
   B. A.D. 284   D. A.D. 330

Test 7—Grade 6 Communications (continued)

Directions: *Read the numbered items below. Then answer questions 9–12.*

---

1. Scientists think that the first people to inhabit North America migrated from Asia some 30,000 years ago.
2. Native Americans eventually populated almost every spot on the continent.
3. After the arrival of Europeans, ways of life for Native Americans began to change.
4. Thousands of Native Americans died from European diseases.
5. Europeans forced Native Americans to move from their lands and work in mines or on farms.

---

9. Suppose that you want to write a report arguing that the arrival of Europeans had a negative effect on Native Americans. Which of the statements above would *best* support your position?
   A. Statement 1
   B. Statement 2
   C. Statement 3
   D. Statement 4

10. Suppose that you had to transfer the events of this passage onto a timeline. What is the *best* way to organize the events in Statements 1, 3, 4, and 5?
   A. in order of importance
   B. according to location
   C. in alphabetical order
   D. in chronological order

11. According to the numbered items, what effect did the arrival of the Europeans have on the Native American population in North America?
   A. They relocated to Asia.
   B. Many died from diseases.
   C. They purchased mines and farms.
   D. Their lifestyle changed very little.

12. If you learned that this passage was written in 1885, what might you reasonably conclude?
   A. The information is probably valid because by 1885 all historical information from this earlier period would have been checked.
   B. The information is probably valid because it was written by an unbiased source who was an expert in early North America.
   C. The information may be flawed because it is old, and scientists may have made more discoveries about early history since 1885.
   D. The information may be flawed because it presents only facts that are negative about the arrival of Europeans.

Name _____ Class _____ Date_____

Test 7—Grade 6 Communications *(continued)*

Directions: *Read the two passages below. Then answer questions 13–16.*

Passage 1: Canada is a very diverse country. Its diversity can be seen at one radio station in the city of Toronto, which broadcasts in 30 languages. One of the largest ethnic groups is the French Canadians of Quebec. Many French Canadians want to break away from Canada to form their own country. They have struggled to have the Canadian government recognize and respect their heritage and language. Their work has resulted in Canada's being a bilingual country, in which both English and French are official languages.

Passage 2: Most immigrants to the United States hold on to some of their old customs. In this way, they can keep a sense of identity in their new land. At the same time, they have helped enrich American culture. Artists, writers, and musicians all add to this mix by combining aspects of American culture with elements from other cultures from around the world.

13. Which statement *best* summarizes the information presented in both passages?
   A. Canada and the United States are countries with large populations made up of a single ethnic group.
   B. Canada and the United States are countries made up of diverse populations with strong cultural identities.
   C. Canada and the United States have immigrant populations that break away from old customs and cultural ties.
   D. Canada and the United States are small countries with populations that speak only a few languages.

14. Suppose that you are giving a speech that describes Canada as a very diverse land. Which statement would *most* effectively support your position?
   A. The population of Canada is scattered across a wide area.
   B. A radio station in Toronto broadcasts in 30 languages.
   C. The largest ethnic group in Canada is French Canadians.
   D. French is widely spoken in the Canadian province of Quebec.

15. According to the passages, how might your life be different if you were Canadian rather than American?
   A. If you were a Canadian, you would not have to struggle to find acceptance for your cultural identity.
   B. If you were a Canadian, you would lack a cultural identity that most people in the United States enjoy.
   C. If you were a Canadian, you might be taught both French and English, which are both official languages in Canada.
   D. If you were a Canadian, you might have to listen to only French-language radio stations.

16. According to the information in both passages, why do *most* immigrants to Canada and the United States preserve many of their original customs?
   A. They never believed they would settle permanently in America or Canada.
   B. They hope to return someday to their native lands.
   C. They want to maintain their cultural identity in their new countries.
   D. They do not like the customs of their adopted countries.

Name _____ Class _____ Date_____

Test 7—Grade 6 Communications *(continued)*

Directions: *Examine the chart below. Then answer questions 17–20.*

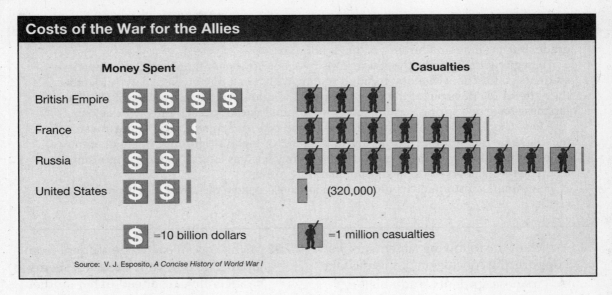

Costs of the War for the Allies

Money Spent — Casualties

British Empire
France
Russia
United States (320,000)

$ =10 billion dollars   = 1 million casualties

Source: V. J. Esposito, *A Concise History of World War I*

17. Which of the following statements *best* characterizes the information on the chart about World War I expenses and casualties?
   A. The United States spent the least on the war and had the fewest casualties.
   B. Although Russia spent less than the British or French did on the war, it had the most casualties.
   C. The British empire spent the most on the war and had the most casualties.
   D. The war cost each country approximately 1 million casualties for every 10 billion dollars spent.

18. Which country spent over $20 billion and had over 7 million casualties?
   A. the British Empire
   B. France
   C. Russia
   D. the United States

19. How much money did the British Empire spend on the World War I effort?
   A. $4 billion
   B. $2 billion
   C. $40 billion
   D. $20 billion

20. According to the chart, which two countries spent about the same amount of money?
   A. France and Russia
   B. the British Empire and France
   C. the British Empire and the United States
   D. Russia and the United States

Test 8—Grade 7 Communications

Directions: *Read the following passage. Then answer questions 1–3.*

> As in America, Japanese elementary and secondary schools run from first to twelfth grade. But as far as similarities go, that is about it.
>
> To begin with, Japan's school year runs two months longer than America's. Japanese students go to school Monday through Friday, with a half day on Saturday. Altogether, they attend 240 days out of the year, compared with the American average of 180. The Japanese have one spring vacation and one summer vacation, each three weeks long....
>
> After school, 80 percent of the students attend *juku*, or "cram school," for extra study, or they have private tutors. They do this to prepare for Japan's rigorous system of entrance exams. Students are free to attend any school they wish as long as they pass its admittance test. The best schools have the most demanding exams....
>
> Few American students would find the Japanese system desirable. But it produces results.

1. Which of the following statements *best* supports the conclusion of this passage?

   A. Japanese students study history, economics, and literature during their high school years.

   B. Ten percent of all Chinese students attend college at Japanese universities, which are highly regarded.

   C. According to a study by Stanford University, more American students are attending colleges today than in the past.

   D. An estimated 94 percent of Japanese students graduate from high school, compared with less than 80 percent of American students.

2. In a comparison chart based on this passage, which of the following column titles would be followed by the *most* entries?

   A. Ways Japanese Education Is Different From American Education

   B. Ways American Education Is Similar to Japanese Education

   C. Ways High School Is Different from Middle School

   D. Ways the Japanese School Day Is Different From the American School Day.

3. Michiko is an exchange student from Japan. She is in your class, but seems to be several years ahead in her studies than you and your classmates. Which of the following is the *best* conclusion you can make about this observation, based on the information in this passage?

   A. It may not be accurate because you cannot compare Michiko's studies to those of her American classmates.

   B. It may be accurate because Michiko has likely spent more time in class and faced stricter requirements than American students her age.

   C. It may be accurate because Michiko may be several years older, as most Japanese students are.

   D. It may not be accurate because Michiko may not be ahead of her classmates in her home country.

Name _____ Class _____ Date_____

Test 8—Grade 7 Communications *(continued)*

Directions: *Read the passage below. Then answer questions 4–7.*

The Great Serpent Mound

The serpent mound in Ohio served a very different purpose from that of Cahokia's pyramid mounds. The twisting, snakelike structure was a cemetery. Called the Great Serpent Mound, it is just one of many similar mounds in Ohio. When you look at these mounds from above, they are shaped like animals. Some served as graves for as many as 1,000 people.

The mounds also hold some of the precious belongings of the Mound Builders. Researchers probing the serpent mounds have found jewelry made of shell and copper, clay statues, and other works of art. Some of these items are made from materials that are not from Ohio. Therefore, researchers believe that the Mound Builders must have been involved in extensive trading.

---

4. You are an archaeologist digging at a site in Illinois. You uncover a beautiful clay pot. After some study, you determine that the paint material used to decorate the pot is not from the Illinois area. Using the same reasoning that is presented in the passage, what would you likely conclude?
   A. The pot is part of a mass grave system in the shape of an animal.
   B. The pot is not part of the Great Serpent Mound.
   C. The pot was painted with materials received by trade.
   D. The pot is from Cahokia's pyramid mounds.

5. For what purpose was the Great Serpent Mound built?
   A. It was used as a temple.
   B. It was used for flood prevention.
   C. It was used as a burial ground.
   D. It was used in religious ceremonies.

6. Jennifer's class studied the Mound Builders, and now she wants to go to Ohio to see the Great Serpent Mound for herself. In an effort to persuade her mother to take her there for a weekend vacation, she pleads, "Mom, please, we have to go! The Great Serpent Mound is the only one ever built." Jennifer's mother could dispute this argument using what piece of information from the passage?
   A. The Great Serpent Mound is no longer in Ohio, but is now in Wisconsin.
   B. The Great Serpent Mound is just one of many similar mounds in Ohio.
   C. The Great Serpent Mound is very similar to Cahokia's pyramid mounds.
   D. The Great Serpent Mound takes so much longer than a weekend to locate.

7. According to the passage, which of the following is a true statement about the Mound Builders?
   A. They did not bury their dead.
   B. A complex system of canals were used to move dirt.
   C. They were known for burying their enemies alive.
   D. They lived in what is now the central part of the United States.

Test 8—Grade 7 Communications (continued)

Directions: *Study the following table. Then answer questions 8–10.*

Rival Plans for Reconstruction				
Plan	**Ten Percent Plan**	**Wade-Davis Bill**	**Johnson Plan**	**Reconstruction Act**
Proposed by	President Abraham Lincoln (1863)	Republicans in Congress (1864)	President Andrew Johnson (1865)	Radical Republicans (1867)
Conditions for former Confederate states to rejoin Union	▪ 10 percent of voters must swear loyalty to Union ▪ Must abolish slavery	▪ Majority of white men must swear loyalty ▪ Former Confederate volunteers cannot vote or hold office	▪ Majority of white men must swear loyalty ▪ Must ratify Thirteenth Amendment ▪ Former Confederate officials may vote and hold office	▪ Must disband state governments ▪ Must write new constitutions ▪ Must ratify Fourteenth Amendment ▪ African American men must be allowed to vote

8. Which of the plans listed in the table would have punished the Confederate states *most* severely?
   A. Ten Percent Plan
   B. Wade-Davis Bill
   C. Johnson Plan
   D. Reconstruction Act

9. If you discovered that this table had been compiled by a former Confederate soldier, what might you suspect about it?
   A. The information is not current because it is over a hundred years old and the soldier is dead.
   B. The information is probably not biased because the soldier has no personal interest in which option is chosen.
   C. The information may be biased because the soldier will be affected directly by the conditions.
   D. The information lacks authority because a soldier is unable to compile facts.

10. You are politically active during the Reconstruction era, and you are making a speech to a group of citizens. In your speech, you argue that slavery must be abolished in the United States, that southern white men must swear loyalty to the Union, and that state governments be excused from re-writing new constitutions. You also say African Americans should not be allowed to vote, but that former Confederate officials can. Which of the following plans would you *most likely* support?
    A. Ten Percent Plan
    B. Johnson Plan
    C. Wade-Davis Bill
    D. Reconstruction Act

Test 8—Grade 7 Communications (continued)

Directions: *Examine the table below. Then answer questions 11–16.*

World War II Deaths

	Military Dead	Civilian Dead
Britain	389,000	65,000
France	211,000	108,000
Soviet Union	7,500,000	15,000,000
United States	292,000	*
Germany	2,850,000	5,000,000
Italy	77,500	100,000
Japan	1,576,000	300,000

*Very small number
All figures are estimates
Source: Henri Michel, *The Second World War*

11. In a report detailing the human losses incurred during the war, Justin wanted to note which country suffered the *most* casualties during World War II. What should his report say about total casualties?

  A. The United States suffered more casualties than any other nation.

  B. The Soviet Union suffered more casualties than any other nation.

  C. Britain suffered more casualties than any other nation.

  D. France suffered more casualties than any other nation.

12. In which country was the difference between the number of military deaths and the number of civilian deaths the *greatest*?

  A. Germany

  B. Japan

  C. Britain

  D. the Soviet Union

13. The number of U.S. civilian dead was such a small number that it wasn't estimated on this table. Which of the following countries had the fewest number of civilian casualties compared to its military dead?

  A. the Soviet Union   **C.** Italy

  B. Germany   **D.** Japan

14. Using this table in a report he gave to his history class, Juan said, "Despite having 292,000 military casualties, the United States had very few civilian casualties. Its ally, the Soviet Union, had exactly 7,500,000 military dead and exactly 15,000,000 civilians dead during the war." What's wrong with this statement?

  A. The figures about the war deaths are incorrect.

  B. The United States had a significant number of civilian deaths.

  C. The figures in the table are estimates, so the number of deaths is not exact.

  D. The Soviet Union suffered more military deaths than civilian deaths.

15. According to the information in the table, which of the following could you *most likely* conclude?

  A. Given the number of military deaths, many battles were probably fought in the United States.

  B. Given the relatively low number of casualties, Italian soldiers were probably highly skilled.

  C. Given the high number of casualties, the Soviet Union probably started the war.

  D. Given the number of civilian deaths, many battles were probably fought in Germany and the Soviet Union.

16. Which of the following countries is estimated to have twice as many military deaths as civilian deaths during World War II?

  A. Britain

  B. France

  C. the United States

  D. Japan

Test 8—Grade 7 Communications (continued)

Directions: *Examine the two graphs below. Then answer questions 17–20.*

American Foreign Trade, 1865–1915

Value in Billions of Dollars

◄ Brand label of an American produce company

Year

Source: *Historical Statistics of the United States*

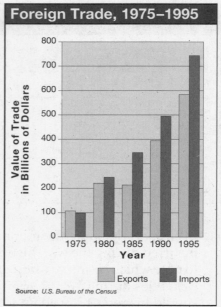

Foreign Trade, 1975–1995

Value of Trade in Billions of Dollars

Year

Exports   Imports

Source: *U.S. Bureau of the Census*

17. Compare both graphs about foreign trade in the United States. Which of the following statements about the graphs is true?

  A. Since 1865, the average value of U.S. foreign trade has remained the same.

  B. In general, from 1865 to 1915 and from 1975 to 1995, the value of U.S. foreign trade has steadily risen.

  C. The difference between the amount the U.S. exports and the amount it imports has been roughly equal since 1856.

  D. Between 1975 and 1995, the U.S. generally exported more goods than it imported.

18. According to the information in the two graphs, what can you accurately conclude about the period between 1916 and 1974?

  A. The trend must have changed because that's what trends do.

  B. The value in billions of dollars continued to increase each year, resulting in an upward, positive trend.

  C. Nothing; information about this time period is not shown in the graphs.

  D. The trend was similar, and the trade deficit increased at or near the same rate between time periods.

19. A trade surplus exists when a country exports more goods than it imports. In which of the following years did the United States have a trade surplus?

  A. 1975   **C.** 1990

  B. 1980   **D.** 1995

20. You have to write a report about U.S. foreign trade, and you want to include the difference between the goods the United States sells to other countries and the goods it buys from other countries over a single ten-year time period. Which graph would be *best* to include in your report and why?

  A. The bar graph would be better to use because it includes trade by imports and exports.

  B. The bar graph would be better to use because its information is more current than the information in the line graph.

  C. The line graph would be better to use because the results include the value of trade in billions of dollars.

  D. The line graph would be better to use because it breaks down trade in ten-year periods.

Name _____ Class _____ Date_____

Test 9—Grade 6 Vocabulary

Directions: *Read the passage. Then answer the questions that follow the passage. Mark the letter of the best answer to each question.*

In ancient China farmers had to figure out how to grow enough food to feed a large <u>population</u>. Over time, farmers cut a series of deep steps into the mountain slopes. Each step, or <u>terrace</u>, increased the amount of farmland that they could <u>cultivate</u>. The terraces also helped prevent soil from wearing away.

This method of farming is still used in China today. Throughout China, terraces climb from the valleys to the tops of <u>rugged</u> mountain ridges. The terraces also help farmers irrigate, or water, their crops. As rain falls, it flows down from one terrace to the next terrace, watering the crops.

---

1. The opposite of the word *rugged* is
   A. rough.
   B. steep.
   C. smooth.
   D. jagged.

2. A synonym for *terrace* is
   A. step.
   B. slope.
   C. earth.
   D. patio.

3. Think about what the word *population* means. What do you think *populus*, the root word of *population*, means?
   A. popular
   B. government
   C. census
   D. people

4. Which phrase could replace "increased the amount of farmland that they could cultivate"?
   A. increased the amount of farmland they could use to raise crops.
   B. increased the amount of farmland they would need to water.
   C. increased the amount of farmland they could use to raise livestock.
   D. increased the amount of farmland they could sell for profit.

Name _____ Class _____ Date_____

Test 9—Grade 6 Vocabulary *(continued)*

Directions: *Read the passage. Then answer the questions that follow the passage. Mark the letter of the best answer to each question.*

Queen Hatshepsut did something unheard of in her time. She boldly declared herself to be Egypt's pharaoh. This royal position usually passed from father to son. Her <u>reign</u> began in 1503 B.C. and lasted twenty-one years. During that time, she helped Egypt <u>regain</u> its wealth through trade with Africa and Asia.

She then devoted herself to a major building program. She rebuilt many of Egypt's great temples. Some of these had been damaged by earlier Asian kings when they ruled Egypt. One of the temples features a series of carvings that tells about important achievements under her leadership.

---

5. A synonym for the word *reign* is
   A. renovation.
   B. throne.
   C. power.
   D. rule.

6. Think about what the word *regain* means. What do you think the prefix *re-* means in the word *regain*?
   A. before
   B. back
   C. with
   D. out

7. Which of the following is a compound word?
   A. achievements
   B. position
   C. leadership
   D. building

8. What two words could be used to describe Hatshepsut?
   A. careful, powerless
   B. weak, confused
   C. ambitious, focused
   D. selfish, powerful

Name _____ Class _____ Date_____

Test 9—Grade 6 Vocabulary *(continued)*

Directions: *Read the passage. Then answer the questions that follow the passage. Mark the letter of the best answer to each question.*

Mansa Musa ruled the West African kingdom of Mali during the 1300s. At that time, Mali was a large and powerful kingdom. It was also a very wealthy kingdom. Despite Mali's vast size and <u>abundant</u> wealth, the kingdom was not well known outside the African continent. However, Mansa Musa's <u>extravagant</u> pilgrimage to Mecca in 1324 told the world about Mali's riches.

On the way to Mecca, Mansa Musa stopped in Cairo, Egypt. Egyptians could hardly believe the <u>spectacular</u> sight. The Mali ruler rode on horseback, joined by 60,000 men, 12,000 slaves, and 80 camels carrying baggage and 24,000 pounds of gold.

Mansa Musa's pilgrimage to Mecca led to greater contact with other Muslim peoples of North Africa and Southwest Asia. The pilgrimage also <u>promoted</u> new trade connections with European nations and kingdoms in North Africa and the Middle East.

---

9. The opposite of the word *abundant* is
   A. plenty.
   B. not enough.
   C. full.
   D. sufficient.

10. A synonym for *extravagant* is
   A. lavish.
   B. cheap.
   C. neutral.
   D. extraction.

11. Think about what the word *spectacular* means. What do you think *spectare*, the root word of *spectacular*, means?
   A. to breathe
   B. to rest for a time
   C. to look at
   D. to think about

12. Which phrase could replace "promoted new trade connections … in North Africa and the Middle East"?
   A. discouraged new trade connections with European nations and kingdoms in North Africa and the Middle East
   B. helped with the growth of new trade connections with European nations and kingdoms in North Africa and the Middle East
   C. publicized new trade connections with European nations and kingdoms in North Africa and the Middle East
   D. led to the failure of any new trade connections with European nations and kingdoms in North Africa and the Middle East

Name _____ Class _____ Date_____

Test 9—Grade 6 Vocabulary (continued)

Directions: *Read the passage. Then answer the questions that follow the passage. Mark the letter of the best answer to each question.*

Over 2,000 years ago, the first emperor to rule over a united China started a huge building project. He wanted to protect China from <u>nomadic</u> tribes in the north. So, he ordered thousands and thousands of Chinese people to build and join a series of walls to defend China. Built of stone, earth, and brick, the Great Wall of China is over 4,000 miles in length. The wall protected China for centuries. It also served as a <u>symbol</u> of the emperor's power.

From east to west, the great wall winds up and down across China's mountains, <u>plateaus</u>, grasslands, and deserts. Today, tourism is a part of China's <u>economy</u> and thousands of visitors come to see the Great Wall of China. From a 40-foot-tall watchtower, the wall looks like a giant dragon, winding its way through the country.

---

13. The opposite of the word *nomadic* is
   A. moving from place to place.
   B. living together.
   C. living independently.
   D. living in one place.

14. Think about what the word *plateau* means. What do you think *plat*, the root word of *plateau*, means?
   A. plentiful
   B. high
   C. flat
   D. rocky

15. A *symbol* is something that
   A. stands for something else.
   B. sends a warning.
   C. serves as a memorial.
   D. becomes a legend.

16. Which means the same as *economy* in the passage?
   A. the ways that goods and services are produced and made available to people
   B. system of beliefs and customs
   C. export of natural resources
   D. preservation of historical monuments

Test 10—Grade 7 Vocabulary

Directions: *Read the passage. Then answer the questions that follow the passage. Mark the letter of the best answer to each question.*

In the late 1500s, five Iroquois nations formed an <u>alliance</u>. These five nations were the Mohawk, Onondaga, Cayuga, Seneca, and Oneida. They often fought with other Native American groups in the eastern woodlands. They believed an alliance would help them to protect themselves and <u>achieve</u> peace.

When meeting to solve a <u>dispute</u>, each tribe in the Iroquois League had one vote. All tribes had to agree on the decision. They used elaborate rituals to choose their leaders. They even convinced leaders in the American colonies to <u>adopt</u> these rituals when the two groups met for discussions.

---

1. A synonym for *alliance* is
   A. friendship.
   B. rivalry.
   C. union.
   D. army.

2. The opposite of the word *achieve* is
   A. attain.
   B. fail.
   C. avoid.
   D. foster.

3. Think about what the word *dispute* means. What do you think the prefix *dis-* means in the word *dispute*?
   A. apart
   B. with
   C. under
   D. before

4. Which means the same as *adopt* in the passage?
   A. to take into one's family
   B. to adjust to a situation
   C. to accept a way of doing something
   D. to reject a new idea

Test 10—Grade 7 Vocabulary (continued)

Directions: *Read the passage. Then answer the questions that follow the passage. Mark the letter of the best answer to each question.*

   Australia is so far from other continents that many of its animals are found nowhere else on Earth. The koala is one of Australia's many <u>unique</u> animals. The koala is a <u>marsupial</u>. Giving birth to one offspring at a time, the mother koala carries the baby in her pouch for seven months. After that time period, the baby clings to its mother's back until it is one year old.
   Because koalas move slowly, forest fire is the greatest threat to their lives. Koalas used to be killed for their fur, but now laws protect them and they <u>thrive</u> in the trees on the eastern coast of Australia. Eucalyptus leaves are koalas' favorite <u>vegetation</u>. Each koala eats as many as three pounds of eucalyptus leaves a day!

---

5. A synonym for the word *thrive* is
   A. theorize.
   B. live.
   C. falter.
   D. flourish.

6. The opposite of the word *unique* is
   A. common.
   B. one of a kind.
   C. singular.
   D. individual.

7. A *marsupial* is an animal that
   A. is found only in Australia.
   B. carries its young in a body pouch.
   C. lives in the rainforest canopy.
   D. is now extinct because of fur trapping.

8. If the definition of the word *vegetation* means "plant or plant life," what do you think *vegetare*, the root word of *vegetation*, means?
   A. to vary
   B. to be green
   C. to locate
   D. to enliven

Name _____ Class _____ Date_____

Test 10—Grade 7 Vocabulary *(continued)*

Directions: *Read the passage. Then answer the questions that follow the passage. Mark the letter of the best answer to each question.*

Japan remained apart from the outside world for many centuries. Japan's isolation, however, did not stop the country from great achievements. One of these achievements was the creation of the world's first novel, *The Tale of Genji*. Lady Murasaki wrote the novel in the early 1000s. The novel's poetry and wordplay reflect the traditions of Japanese art.

The novel focuses on Prince Genji. It also tells about life in the Japanese imperial court. Lady Murasaki knew firsthand about this way of life. She wrote the novel when she served as a lady of the court. Her father's connection to a certain clan helped him arrange the court appointment for his daughter. Lady Murasaki lived at court until her death.

9. A synonym for the word *isolation* is
   A. socialization.
   B. separation.
   C. island.
   D. diffusion.

10. Think about what the word *reflect* means. What do you think the prefix *re-* means in the word *reflect*?
   A. against
   B. back
   C. again
   D. with

11. Which of the following does the word *imperial* relate to?
   A. peril
   B. impartial
   C. empire
   D. imperative

12. Which of the following is a compound word?
   A. wordplay
   B. achievement
   C. remained
   D. connection

Test 10—Grade 7 Vocabulary (continued)

Directions: *Read the passage. Then answer the questions that follow the passage. Mark the letter of the best answer to each question.*

The ancient religion of Buddhism was founded in India. According to Buddhist tradition, the founder of the religion was a prince named Siddhartha Gautama, an Indian <u>philosopher</u> who became known as the Buddha, or "Enlightened One." Through his sermons and teachings, the Buddha <u>converted</u> many people to the Buddhist religion.

Many legends exist about the Buddha's life. One of these legends is about his birth. Before the Buddha was born, his mother dreamed that a white elephant came down from heaven and entered her womb. Hindu priests told her that the dream meant she would give birth to a great world leader.

Prince Siddhartha grew up in a palace. He lived in great luxury because of his family's wealth and royal position. Siddhartha's family belonged to the high warrior <u>caste</u>. When the prince visited the capital of his father's kingdom, he saw many old and sick people. The sight of the people's suffering changed the prince's life. He gave up his life of power and wealth and went up into the hills to <u>meditate</u>. He sought truth and enlightenment as a way to rise above suffering.

---

13. A synonym for *caste* is
   A. warrior.
   B. class.
   C. belief.
   D. system.

14. The opposite of the word *meditate* is
   A. think about.
   B. reflect.
   C. disregard.
   D. consider.

15. Think about what the word *philosopher* means. What do you think *sophos*, one of the root words of *philosopher*, means?
   A. focused
   B. sophisticated
   C. wise
   D. obedient

16. Which phrase could replace "the Buddha converted many people to the Buddhist religion"?
   A. the Buddha conveyed ideas about the Buddhist religion to many people
   B. the Buddha changed what people thought about Buddhism
   C. the Buddha turned many people away from the Buddhist religion
   D. the Buddha persuaded many people to adopt the Buddhist religion

Test 11—Grade 6 Writing Test

Directions: *Read the following passage. Then fill out the information chart.*

Deep in the heart of Siberia is a forest reserve called the Olekminsky Zapovednik. Nearly 90 percent of the reserve is covered with cedar, fir, spruce, pine, larch, and birch trees.

Rivers and creeks flow through the hills and low mountains of the reserve. The forests, meadows, riverbanks, and wetlands provide habitats for nearly 200 species of birds. Many of these birds are rare, including the golden eagle, osprey, and peregrine falcon.

The forest reserve is also home to a variety of mammals. Brown bears roam the forests in search of berries. In the fall, reindeer gather in herds near the tall larch trees. In the summer, moose meet at the creeks and rivers. Other mammals living in the forest include the Siberian sable, flying squirrel, lynx, wolverine, and wolf.

Characteristics	Olekminsky Zapovednik
What is it?	
Where is it located?	
What animals live there?	
What vegetation grows there?	
What are some of its geographical features?	

Test 11—Grade 6 Writing (continued)

Directions: *Read the passage. Then write a summary in your own words of the main ideas presented in the passage. Begin your summary with a topic sentence.*

In France, all children between the ages of 6 and 16 are required to attend school. Children attend elementary school for five years, from ages 6 to 11. Then they go on to middle school, which is called college and lasts for four years. At 16 years of age, children must leave college, whether or not they receive a certificate of completion.

After college, a second level of secondary education is available to students, but not required. Students may go to either a vocational high school or a general high school, both of which are called *lycées*. In a vocational high school, students receive job training in business, farming, a craft, or a trade. In a general high school, students focus on academic subjects and prepare to enter universities. During this three-year course, students work hard. They may take classes up to 30 hours a week and have three hours of homework a day. At the end, they take a *baccalauréat* examination, which is very difficult to pass. About one third of the students fail. A person must have a *baccalauréat* diploma to be admitted to a university.

_____

_____

_____

_____

_____

_____

_____

_____

_____

_____

_____

_____

_____

_____

_____

_____

_____

Test 11—Grade 6 Writing (continued)

Directions: *Think about a significant event in your life or the life of someone you know. Then write one or two paragraphs describing the event and its effect on your life or your acquaintance's life. Use specific details to create a picture in words, describing the event and what makes it significant.*

_____

_____

_____

_____

_____

_____

_____

_____

_____

_____

_____

_____

_____

_____

_____

_____

_____

_____

_____

_____

_____

_____

_____

_____

_____

_____

Test 11—Grade 6 Writing (continued)

Directions: *Write a proposal to create a classroom website to connect with other sixth grade classrooms around the world. Consider some of the following information in your proposal:*

- How would your class and the other classes benefit from a cyberspace connection?
- What would some of the challenges be in creating the website?
- What would the primary purpose be for the site?
- What kinds of information might you and your classmates be able to exchange with other 6th grade students around the world?
- How does your proposal relate to policies your school has about using the Internet?

Prepare an outline of the ideas you will use in your proposal.

Use the following form to begin your outline:

I. Topic sentence _____

   A. Supporting detail _____

   B. Supporting detail _____

   C. Supporting detail _____

II. Concluding sentence _____

After completing your outline, use it to write a paragraph explaining your proposal.

_____

_____

_____

_____

_____

_____

_____

_____

_____

_____

_____

_____

_____

_____

Test 12—Grade 7 Writing

Directions: *Read the following passage. Then complete the activity.*

> By 2001, twelve European countries had adopted the euro. The euro is the official currency of the European Union. Some countries, including the United Kingdom, chose not to adopt the euro. The debate for and against the euro continues today.
>
> The pro-euro group in Britain claims that multinational businesses would benefit from the euro. They believe that a single currency will lead to a single European market. If the euro is not adopted, the pro-euro group fears that Britain will lose even more jobs to other countries.
>
> The anti-euro group claims that the euro is weak and unstable. Furthermore, most of Britain's international trade is carried out in United States dollars. The anti-euro group believes that Britain does not need a common currency to have a successful economy.

Which view would you support? Plan what you would say in a debate or discussion about the issue. Then prepare a paragraph outline of the ideas you will use in your response.

Use the following form to begin your paragraph outline:

I. Topic sentence _____

   A. Supporting detail _____

   B. Supporting detail _____

   C. Supporting detail _____

II. Concluding sentence_____

After completing your outline, use it to write a paragraph explaining your position.

_____

_____

_____

_____

_____

_____

_____

_____

_____

_____

_____

_____

_____

Test 12—Grade 7 Writing (continued)

Directions: *Read the passage. Then write a brief essay that compares your life at home to that of a child living in a feudal castle. Keep in mind that you should include details that show similarities and differences between the two subjects.*

Kings and feudal lords built castles to serve as their homes and as fortresses. From his castle, a feudal lord could defend his lands. Besides the lord's family, servants, and a chaplain, the castle was home to soldiers who kept guard and were ready to fight when necessary. Horses, pigs, and other animals also lived inside the castle. In winter, castles were often damp, cold, and drafty. Candles and torches provided light, and fires and fireplaces provided heat.

The castle household arose at daybreak. Servants lit fires in the kitchen and the great hall. After praying in the chapel, the lord and lady ate breakfast and worked around the castle. Their children had lessons with tutors. At the midday meal, people entertained the household with songs and stories. Supper was served in the late afternoon, and the household usually went to bed early.

_____

_____

_____

_____

_____

_____

_____

_____

_____

_____

_____

_____

_____

_____

_____

_____

_____

Test 12—Grade 7 Writing *(continued)*

Directions: *Choose an environmental issue that has been in the news recently, such as pollution, use of natural resources, or endangered species. Choose one side of the issue, then write one or two paragraphs to persuade people toward your point of view. Think about the pros and cons of your argument. Try to predict and address the strongest arguments against your position.*

_____

_____

_____

_____

_____

_____

_____

_____

_____

_____

_____

_____

_____

_____

_____

_____

_____

_____

_____

_____

_____

_____

_____

_____

Name _____ Class _____ Date_____

Test 12—Grade 7 Writing (continued)

Directions: *Read the passage. Then complete the activity that follows.*

The culture of Europe includes a long and magnificent tradition in art. European art has had greater influence throughout the world than the art of any other continent. Perhaps the most famous European artist of the 1900s is Pablo Picasso of Spain. He strongly influenced many artists of his time as well as later artists.

Picasso developed a number of original styles in painting. One is called his Blue Period, during which he painted sad figures in shades of blue. During the Rose Period, Picasso's paintings, done in shades of rose, were happier. But the style that had the greatest impact on modern art was cubism. Picasso's painting *Les Demoiselles d'Avignon* (1907) shows five female figures that are broken into geometric shapes with sharp edges. The painting marked a major change in Western ideas about beauty and harmony in art.

The writer of this article shows bias in some of the statements about Picasso and his influence on art. Rewrite the two paragraphs, removing or replacing the biased words and phrases with unbiased words and phrases.

_____

_____

_____

_____

_____

_____

_____

_____

_____

_____

_____

_____

_____

_____

_____

_____

Diagnosing Readiness Tests
Answer Key

Test 1—Grade 6 Geographic Literacy

1. C	2. A	3. B	4. C	5. A
6. C	7. B	8. C	9. A	10. B
11. A	12. C	13. C	14. B	15. A
16. C				

Test 2—Grade 7 Geographic Literacy

1. C	2. B	3. A	4. C	5. B
6. C	7. C	8. C	9. C	10. A
11. C	12. A	13. B	14. B	15. D
16. C	17. A			

Test 3—Grade 6 Visual Analysis

1. B	2. A	3. C	4. D	5. B
6. B	7. D	8. C	9. D	

Test 4—Grade 7 Visual Analysis

1. B	2. C	3. C	4. D	5. C
6. C	7. D	8. C	9. A	10. D

Test 5—Grade 6 Critical Thinking and Reading

1. A	2. B	3. D	4. A	5. A
6. C	7. D	8. A	9. D	10. A
11. B	12. B	13. C	14. D	15. D
16. D	17. A	18. C	19. B	20. A

Test 6—Grade 7 Critical Thinking and Reading

1. B	2. A	3. D	4. B	5. C
6. B	7. C	8. C	9. C	10. A
11. A	12. D	13. C	14. A	15. C
16. B				

Test 7—Grade 6 Communications

1. B	2. D	3. B	4. A	5. B
6. C	7. B	8. B	9. D	10. D
11. B	12. C	13. B	14. B	15. C
16. C	17. B	18. C	19. C	20. D

Test 8—Grade 7 Communications

1. D	2. A	3. B	4. C	5. C
6. B	7. D	8. D	9. C	10. B
11. B	12. D	13. D	14. C	15. D
16. B	17. B	18. C	19. A	20. A

Diagnosing Readiness Tests

Answer Key (continued)

Test 9—Grade 6 Vocabulary

1. C	2. A	3. D	4. A	5. D
6. B	7. C	8. C	9. B	10. A
11. C	12. B	13. D	14. C	15. A
16. A				

Test 10—Grade 7 Vocabulary

1. C	2. B	3. A	4. C	5. D
6. A	7. B	8. D	9. B	10. B
11. C	12. A	13. B	14. C	15. C
16. D				

Test 11—Grade 6 Writing

Page 53 Students' tables should contain the following information in the Olekminsky Zapovednik column:

What is it?—A forest reserve

Where is it located?—In the heart of Siberia

What animals live there?—Many birds and mammals have habitats there, including rare birds such as the golden eagle, osprey, and peregrine falcon. Mammals include reindeer, moose, brown bears, Siberian sable, flying squirrel, lynx, wolverine, and wolf.

What vegetation grows there?—Vegetation includes forests, meadows, and grasses. The many different varieties of trees include cedar, fir, spruce, pine, larch, and birch.

What are some of its geographical features?—Wetlands, low mountains, hills, rivers, creeks are some of the reserve's features.

Page 54 Summaries should include a topic sentence and, in students' own words, clearly state the main ideas presented in the passage. Possible topic sentence: In France, all children are required to take three levels of schooling, with an option to go on to a university after the third level.

Page 55 Descriptive paragraphs should include specific details that describe an event in the life of the student or an acquaintance of the student.

Page 56 Outlines should follow a hierarchy of ideas and supporting details. Paragraphs should make a logical argument for creating a classroom website to communicate with other sixth grade students around the world.

Diagnosing Readiness Tests

Answer Key (continued)

Test 12—Grade 7 Writing

Page 57 Outlines should follow a hierarchy of ideas and supporting details. Paragraphs should make a logical argument for or against the United Kingdom's adoption of the euro.

Page 58 Students should evaluate specific characteristics of similarities and differences in their essays.

Page 59 Students should clearly state their point of view and present supporting evidence in a persuasive or convincing way.

Page 60 *Possible revision for paragraph on Picasso:*

The culture of Europe includes a long tradition in art. European art has had influence throughout the world. One of the most famous European artists of the 1900s was Pablo Picasso of Spain. He influenced many artists of his time as well as later artists.

Picasso developed a number of original styles in painting. One is called his Blue Period, during which he painted figures in shades of blue. During the Rose Period, Picasso's paintings were done in shades of rose. But the style that had a significant impact on modern art was cubism. Picasso's painting *Les Demoiselles d'Avignon* (1907) shows five female figures that are broken into geometric shapes with sharp edges. The painting marked a change in Western ideas about beauty and harmony in art.

Correlation to Program Resources

The following chart correlates test items in the Diagnosing Readiness Tests with specific skills. Then the chart directs you to resources in the program where students can practice those skills.

Diagnosing Readiness Correlations	Test Items	World Studies Africa	World Studies Ancient World	World Studies Asia and the Pacific	World Studies Europe and Russia
Communications					
Using Reliable Information	Grade 6: 3, 12 Grade 7: 3, 9	TE: p. 153 TR: p. 15, 31	TE: p. 112 TR: p. 31	TR: pp. 17, 33, 127, 284, 357 SE: pp. 18-19 TE: pp 18-19	TE: p. 64 TR: pp. 15, 133
Transferring Information from One Medium to Another	Grade 6: 5, 6, 7, 8, 10, 17, 18, 20 Grade 7: 2, 8, 11, 12, 13, 14, 16, 18,19	TE: p. 169	TE: p. 140 TR: pp. 165-166, 213-214, 256-257, 303-304, 400-401	TR: pp. 397, 398	SE: pp. 152-153 TE: pp. 124, 152-153
Synthesizing Information	Grade 6: 11, 13, 14, 16, 19 Grade 7: 5, 7, 15, 17, 18, 20	TE: p. 52 TR: p. 113	TE: p. 78	SE: pp. 160-161 TE: pp. 160-161 TR: pp. 17, 22, 348	TE: p. 178 TR: p. 170

SE: Student Edition   TE: Teacher's Edition   TR: All-in-One Teaching Resources

World Studies Foundations of Geography	World Studies Latin America	World Studies Medieval Times to Today	World Studies United States and Canada	World Studies Eastern Hemisphere	World Studies Western Hemisphere
SE: pp. 14-15 TE: pp. 14-15 TR: pp. 30, 36, 72	TE: p. 118 TR: 14, 29, 258	SE: pp. 42-43 TE: pp. 42-43 TR: 17	TE: p. 87 TR: pp. 13, 29, 220	SE: 14-15, 584-585 TE: 14-15, 202, 363, 379, 584-585	SE: pp. 14-15 TE: pp. 14-15, 227, 446
TE: p. 53 TR: pp. 27-29, 35, 129-130, 132-133, 183-184	TE: p. 170 TR: pp. 73-75, 114, 116-117, 249-250, 337-338	SE: pp. 16-17 TE: pp. 16-17	TE: p. 45 TR: pp. 82-84, 116-117, 165, 212, 261-262	SE: 290-291 TE: 53, 262, 290-291, 517	TE: pp. 53, 183, 498
TE: p. 100	SE: pp. 186-187 TE: pp. 186-187 TR: p. 336	TE: p. 214 TR: p. 160	TE: p. 112 TR: pp. 16, 18, 95, 160, 211, 311	SE: 726-727 TE: 100, 316, 400, 726-727	SE: pp. 514-515 TE: pp. 100, 250, 514-515

SE: Student Edition   TE: Teacher's Edition   TR: All-in-One Teaching Resources

Diagnosing Readiness Correlations (continued)	Test Items	World Studies Africa	World Studies Ancient World	World Studies Asia and the Pacific	World Studies Europe and Russia
Supporting a Position	Grade 6: 1, 2, 4, 9, 15 Grade 7: 1, 4, 6, 10, 20	TE: p. 113 TR: p. 17	TE: p. 221 TR: p. 11	TR: pp. 13, 432	SE: pp. 98-99 TE: pp. 98-99 TR: pp. 11, 17
Critical Thinking and Reading					
Identifying Main Ideas/ Summarizing	Grade 6: 8, 20 Grade 7: 9	SE: pp. 126, 136, 137, 142, 144, 150, 152, 176–177 TE: pp. 126b, 136, 142, 150, 176–177 TR: pp. 301, 302, 303, 351	SE: pp. 47, 48, 51, 58-59, 60, 61, 64, 136, 138, 141, 143, 144, 145, 148, 149, 152, 155, 158, 160, 162 TE: pp. 47, 58-59, 60, 136B, 138, 146, 151, 158 TR: pp. 20, 164, 297-299	SE: pp. 42-43, 52, 54, 59, 61, 62, 68, 71, 218, 230, 235, 238, 239 TE: pp. 42-43, 52b, 54, 59, 61, 68, 71, 218b, 230, 238 TR: pp. 18, 22, 166, 431	SE: pp. 82, 84, 87, 91 93, 100, 102 TE: 73, 82b, 84, 91, 100 TR: pp. 172, 227, 229
Sequencing	Grade 6: 5 Grade 7: 6	SE: pp. 64–65, 190, 200, 203, 208, 209 TE: pp. 52, 64–65, 190b, 200, 208 TR: p. 169	SE: pp. 14-15, 208, 210, 213, 215, 218, 220, 223, 224, 226, 228, 229, 231, 233, 236, 239, 240 TE: pp. 14-15, 208B, 210, 218, 224, 229, 236 TR: pp. 117, 395-396	SE: pp. 120, 122, 124, 130, 131 TE: pp. 120b, 122, 130, 131 TR: pp. 435, 441	TE: p. 57

SE: Student Edition   TE: Teacher's Edition   TR: All-in-One Teaching Resources

World Studies Foundations of Geography	World Studies Latin America	World Studies Medieval Times to Today	World Studies United States and Canada	World Studies Eastern Hemisphere	World Studies Western Hemisphere
TE: p. 131 TR: p. 9	TE: p. 146 TR: 11, 245-246, 346	TE: p. 158 TR: pp. 13, 19	TE: p. 157 TR: pp. 9, 15	SE: 236-237 TE: 131, 236-237, 461	TE: pp. 131, 295, 474
SE: pp. 112, 114, 115, 119, 120, 122, 125, 128, 131, 132 TE: pp. 76, 112B, 114, 120, 128 TR: pp. 18, 256-258	SE: pp. 57, 59, 61, 126, 134, 136, 139, 142, 146, 147, 148, 153, 154 TE: pp. 57, 84, 126B, 134, 142, 148 TR: pp. 161, 287-289	SE: pp. 60, 62, 65, 70, 72, 78, 81, 98-99 TE: pp. 60b, 62, 70, 78, 98-99 TR: pp. 161, 199, 201	SE: pp. 74, 76, 79, 81, 82-83, 84, 86, 88, 89, 91, 92, 178-179 TE: pp. 74B, 76, 82-83, 84, 89, 178-179 TR: pp. 18, 207-209	SE: 112, 114, 115, 119, 120, 122, 125, 128, 131, 132, 220, 222, 225, 229, 231, 238, 240, 474, 484, 485, 490, 492, 498, 500, 524-525, 608-609, 618, 620	SE: pp. 112, 114, 115, 119, 120, 122, 125, 128, 131, 132, 212, 214, 217, 219, 220-221, 222, 224, 227, 229, 230, 316-317, 385, 387, 389, 391, 454, 462, 464, 467, 470, 474, 475, 476, 481, 482
SE: pp. 90, 92, 95, 96, 97, 101, 104, 106, 108 TE: pp. 18, 90B, 92, 96, 104 TR: p. 221, 222	SE: pp. 62-63 TE: pp. 62-63 TR: p. 164	SE: pp. 116, 118, 120, 126, 131, 133, 136, 140, 142 TE: pp. 81, 116b, 118, 126, 133, 140 TR: pp. 285, 286	TE: p. 183 TR: pp. 79-81	SE: 90, 92, 95, 96, 97, 101, 104, 106, 108, 412-413, 538, 548, 551, 556, 557, 686, 688, 690, 696, 697	SE: pp. 90, 92, 95, 96, 97, 101, 104, 106, 108, 390-391

SE: Student Edition   TE: Teacher's Edition   TR: All-in-One Teaching Resources

Diagnosing Readiness Correlations (continued)	Test Items	World Studies Africa	World Studies Ancient World	World Studies Asia and the Pacific	World Studies Europe and Russia
Identifying Cause and Effect/Making Predictions	Grade 6: 6, 18 Grade 7: 3	SE: pp. 104, 110, 113, 118, 119 TE: pp. 104b, 110, 118, 144 TR: 221, 222, 223, 259, 260	SE: pp. 106, 108, 110, 113, 116, 119, 120, 121, 123, 125, 128, 130, 132 TE: pp. 27, 106B, 108, 116, 121, 128 TR: pp. 16, 209, 249-252	SE: pp. 66, 67, 170, 184, 188, 190, 192, 195, 200, 201, 208, 209 TE: pp. 66-67, 170b, 184, 190, 195, 200, 208 TR: pp. 18, 169, 202, 275, 285, 389-392	TE: p. 48 TR: p. 17
Making Inferences/ Drawing Conclusions	Grade 6: 4, 7, 17 Grade 7: 1, 5, 8, 10, 11	TE: p. 181	SE: pp. 194-195 TE: pp. 194-195 TR: pp. 9, 348	SE: pp. 128-129 TE: pp. 128-129 TR: pp. 167-169, 235- 237	TE: p. 157
Making Valid Generalizations	Grade 6: 3 Grade 7: 12	TE: p. 20	SE: pp. 144-145 TR: p. 302	TE: p. 186	TE: p. 87
Distinguishing Fact and Opinion	Grade 6: 10 Grade 7: 16	SE: pp. 116–117 TE: pp. 116–117 TR: p. 263	TE: p. 123	TR: pp. 435, 441	TE: p. 104

SE: Student Edition   TE: Teacher's Edition   TR: All-in-One Teaching Resources

World Studies Foundations of Geography	World Studies Latin America	World Studies Medieval Times to Today	World Studies United States and Canada	World Studies Eastern Hemisphere	World Studies Western Hemisphere
SE: pp. 126-127 TE: pp. 30, 126-127 TR: pp. 14, 261	SE: pp. 72, 74, 77, 79, 82, 83, 86, 87, 88, 92 TE: pp. 72B, 74, 78, 82, 87 TR: pp. 15, 199-201	SE: pp. 68-69, 88, 90, 95, 100, 102, 108, 110 TE: pp. 68-69, 88b, 90, 100, 108 TR: pp. 18, 237-239	TE: p. 40 TR: pp. 14, 307	SE: pp. 126-127, 452, 458, 461, 466, 467, 632-633, 736, 750, 754, 756, 758, 761, 766, 767, 784, 785	SE: pp. 126-127, 400, 402, 405, 407, 410, 411, 414, 415, 416, 420
TE: p. 12 TR: p. 7	SE: pp. 114-115 TE: pp. 114-115 TR: p. 244	TE: p. 234	TE: p. 78	SE: pp. 694-695, TE: pp. 12, 295, 529, 694-695	SE: pp. 442-443 TE: pp. 12, 216, 442-443
SE: pp. 102-103 TR: p. 225	TE: p. 12	TE: p. 13	TE: p. 27 TR: p. 305	SE: pp. 102-103 TE: pp. 102-103, 225, 368, 752	SE: pp. 102-103 TE: pp. 165, 340
TE: p. 107	SE: pp. 80-81 TE: pp. 80-81 TR: pp. 77, 204	SE: p. 138-139 TE: p. 138-139	TE: p. 136	SE: pp. 464-465 TE: pp. 107, 242, 464-465	SE: pp. 408-409 TE: pp. 107, 274, 408-409

SE: Student Edition   TE: Teacher's Edition   TR: All-in-One Teaching Resources

Diagnosing Readiness Correlations (continued)	Test Items	World Studies Africa	World Studies Ancient World	World Studies Asia and the Pacific	World Studies Europe and Russia
Comparing and Contrasting	Grade 6: 1, 12 Grade 7: 7, 14	SE: pp. 76, 78, 81, 84, 86, 90–91, 92, 94, 97, 99 TE: pp. 76b, 78, 84, 90–91, 92, 97 TR: 221, 222, 223, 226	SE: pp. 234-235 TE: pp. 234-235 TR: p. 399	SE: pp. 142, 148, 153, 154, 156, 162 TE: 142b, 148, 154, 162 TR: pp. 343-345	SE: pp. 164, 174, 178, 181, 184, 189, 192, 198, 202 TE: pp. 164b, 174, 181, 189, 198 TR: pp. 329, 330, 331
Analyzing Primary and Secondary Sources	Grade 6: 13, 19 Grade 7: 2, 4	SE: pp. 206–207 TE: pp. 206–207 TR: pp. 127-128, 177-183, 233-234, 270-273, 317, 318, 363-369, 399, 407-408	TE: p. 161 TR: pp. 123-124, 169, 218-219, 262-266, 301, 308, 355, 404-410	TE: p. 132 TR: pp. 133- 135, 210, 211, 243, 279, 280, 355, 356, 403-406, 444, 445	TE: p. 94 TR: pp. 131-132, 182-197, 237-241, 292-295, 345
Recognizing Bias and Propaganda	Grade 6: 2, 11 Grade 7: 16	TE: p. 204	TE: p. 198	SE: pp. 110-111 TE: pp. 110-111 TR: p. 272	TE: p. 200
Identifying Frame of Reference and Point of View	Grade 6: 9, 14, 20 Grade 7: 13	TE: p. 95	TE: p. 49	TE: p. 89	SE: 196-197 TE: 196-197
Decision Making	Grade 6: 16 Grade 7: 15	SE: pp. 148–149 TE: pp. 148–149	TE: p. 191	TE: p. 232	TE: p. 143

SE: Student Edition   TE: Teacher's Edition   TR: All-in-One Teaching Resources

World Studies Foundations of Geography	World Studies Latin America	World Studies Medieval Times to Today	World Studies United States and Canada	World Studies Eastern Hemisphere	World Studies Western Hemisphere
SE: pp. 58, 60, 62, 66, 67, 68, 71, 74, 76, 79, 80, 81, 84 TE: pp. 44, 58B, 60, 67, 74, 80 TR: pp. 123, 177-179	SE: pp. 140-141, 158, 166, 169, 172, 173, 177, 178, 179, 181, 185, 188, 191, 194 TE: pp. 140-141, 158B, 166, 173, 179, 188 TR: pp. 240, 292, 331-333	SE: pp. 188, 190, 194, 198, 200, 204, 208, 212, 214 TE: pp. 48, 18b, 190, 198, 204, 212 TR: pp. 379, 380, 381	SE: pp. 96, 110, 113, 116, 117, 121, 123, 126, 129, 132, 133, 137, 138 TE: pp. 96B, 110, 117, 126, 133 TR: pp. 251-253	SE: pp. 58, 60, 62, 66, 67, 68, 71, 74, 76, 79, 80, 81, 84, 302, 312, 313, 316, 319, 322, 327, 330, 336, 340, 424, 426, 429, 432, 434, 438-439, 440, 442, 445, 447, 708, 714, 719, 720, 722, 728	SE: pp. 58, 60, 62, 66, 67, 68, 71, 74, 76, 79, 80, 81, 84, 234, 248, 251, 254, 255, 259, 261, 264, 267, 270, 271, 275, 276, 468-469, 486, 494, 497, 500, 501, 505, 506, 507, 509, 513, 516, 519, 522
TE: p. 122 TR: pp. 92-93, 138-142, 188-194, 230-231, 268-272	TE: p. 52 TR: pp. 123-125, 169-172, 209-213, 255-257, 298-300, 344-345	TE: p. 95 TR: pp. 99-101, 102, 103, 130, 131-132, 170, 171, 172, 209-211, 248-251, 342-343, 344-346, 391, 392-393, 435, 436	TE: p. 51 TR: pp. 122-125, 172-181, 218, 219, 268, 269, 320-322	SE: pp. 554-555 TE: pp. 122, 232, 554-555, 613	TE: pp. 122, 189, 380
TE: p. 94	TE: p. 54	TE: p. 165	TE: p. 156	SE: pp. 676-677 TE: pp. 94, 338, 552, 676-677	TE: pp. 94, 294, 382
TE: p. 69	TE: p. 177	TE: p. 136	SE: pp. 16-17 TE: pp. 16-17 TR: p. 115	SE: 334-335 TE: pp. 69, 334-335, 443, 655	SE: pp. 344-345 TE: pp. 69, 315, 344-345
TE: p. 83	TE: p. 137	TE: p. 202	TE: p. 79	SE: pp. 496-497 TE: 83, 281, 798	TE: pp. 83, 217, 465

SE: Student Edition   TE: Teacher's Edition   TR: All-in-One Teaching Resources

Diagnosing Readiness Correlations (continued)	Test Items	World Studies Africa	World Studies Ancient World	World Studies Asia and the Pacific	World Studies Europe and Russia
Problem Solving	Grade 6: 15, 16 Grade 7: 15	TE: p. 99	TE: p. 239 TR: p. 17	TE: p. 40	SE: pp. 60-61 TE: pp. 60-61
Geography Literacy					
Using the Cartographer's Tools	Grade 6: 1, 2, 3, 5, 6, 7, 9, 10, 16 Grade 7: 4, 5, 6, 7, 8, 10, 11, 12, 13, 15, 16	TE: p. 29 See MapMaster Skills Handbook in SE, TE, and TR.	TE: p. 18 See MapMaster Skills Handbook in SE, TE, and TR.	TR: p. 242 See MapMaster Skills Handbook in SE, TE, and TR.	See MapMaster Skills Handbook in SE, TE, and TR.
Analyzing and Interpreting Special-Purpose Maps	Grade 6: 4, 8, 11, 12, 13, 14, 15 Grade 7: 1, 2, 3, 9, 14, 17	TE: p. 40 See MapMaster Skills Handbook in SE, TE, and TR.	SE: pp. 96-97 TE: pp. 96-97 TR: pp. 122, 212, 217 See MapMaster Skills Handbook in SE, TE, and TR.	TR: pp. 171, 234, 239, 240, 241, 353, 400, 440 See MapMaster Skills Handbook in SE, TE, and TR.	See MapMaster Skills Handbook in SE, TE, and TR.
Visual Analysis					
Analyzing Graphic Data	Grade 6: 1, 2, 3, 4, 5, 6, 7, 8, 9 Grade 7: 1, 2, 3, 4, 5	SE: pp. 24-25 TE: 24-25 TR: 313, 360-362, 405, 411	SE: pp. 126-127 TE: pp. 126-127 TR: p. 62	SE: pp. 206-207, 236-237 TE: pp. 206-207, 236-237 TR: pp. 64, 277, 395	TE: pp. 152-153 TR: pp. 287, 289, 290, 291

SE: Student Edition   TE: Teacher's Edition   TR: All-in-One Teaching Resources

World Studies Foundations of Geography	World Studies Latin America	World Studies Medieval Times to Today	World Studies United States and Canada	World Studies Eastern Hemisphere	World Studies Western Hemisphere
TE: p. 118 TR: p. 15	TE: p. 111	TE: p. 104	TE: p. 57	SE: pp. 198-199 TE: pp. 118, 198-199, 447, 606	TE: pp. 118, 195, 439
TE: p. 43 TR: pp. 43-45, 52, 53, 71, 79, 80, 81, 82, 83, 84, 85-90, 134	TE: p. 104 TR: p. 122 See MapMaster Skills Handbook in SE, TE, and TR.	TE: p. 39 TR: p. 247 See MapMaster Skills Handbook in SE, TE, and TR.	See MapMaster Skills Handbook in SE, TE, and TR.	See MapMaster Skills Handbook in SE, TE, and TRs.	See MapMaster Skills Handbook in SE, TE, and TRs.
SE: pp. 72-73 TE: pp. 72-73 TR: pp. 46-50, 54, 135, 137, 182, 224, 266-267 See MapMaster Skills Handbook in SE and TE.	SE: pp. 22-23 TE: pp. 22-23 TR: pp. 115, 251, 341 See MapMaster Skills Handbook in SE, TE, and TR.	SE: pp. 178-179 TE: pp. 178-179 TR: pp. 97, 98, 169, 434 See MapMaster Skills Handbook in SE, TE, and TR.	TR: pp. 94, 121, 171, 263, 264, 316 See MapMaster Skills Handbook in SE, TE, and TR.	See MapMaster Skills Handbook in SE, TE, and TRs.	See MapMaster Skills Handbook in SE, TE, and TRs.
SE: pp. 48-49 TE: pp. 48-49, 65 TR: pp. 127-136	TE: p. 66 TR: 60, 252	SE: pp. 196-197, 236-237 TE: pp. 236-237 TR: pp. 390-433	SE: pp. 62-63, 82-83, 124-125 TE: pp. 62-63, 82-83, 124-125	SE: pp. 48-49, 290-291, 372-373, 772-773, 802-803	SE: pp. 48-49, 200-201, 220-221, 262-263

SE: Student Edition   TE: Teacher's Edition   TR: All-in-One Teaching Resources

Diagnosing Readiness Correlations (continued)	Test Items	World Studies Africa	World Studies Ancient World	World Studies Asia and the Pacific	World Studies Europe and Russia
Analyzing Images	Grade 6: 1, 2, 3, 4 Grade 7: 6, 7, 8, 9, 10	TE: p. 210 TR: pp. 125, 175, 176	TE: p. 45	TE: p. 47	TE: p. 41
Vocabulary					
Using Social Studies Terms Correctly	Grade 6: 1-11 Grade 7: 1-16	SE: pp. 158, 166, 168, 171, 172, 178, 181 TE: pp. 158b, 166, 171, 178 TR: 129, 184, 236, 275, 319, 371, 410	SE: pp. 68, 70, 72, 75, 76, 78, 81, 82 86, 87, 90, 93, 95, 98, 101, 102, 166, 168, 172, 173, 174, 176, 180, 181, 182, 185, 188, 189, 193, 196, 197, 200 TE: pp. 68B, 70, 76 82, 90, 98, 166B, 168, 174, 181, 188, 196	SE: pp. 76, 78, 80, 86, 88, 94, 96, 100, 103, 108, 112, 116 TE: 76b, 78, 86, 94b, 96, 103, 112 TR: pp. 136, 173, 213, 244, 281, 358, 407, 448	SE: 110, 122, 125, 130, 136, 138, 142, 145, 146, 154, 158 TE: pp. 110b, 122, 130, 138, 145, 154 TR: pp. 135, 200, 243, 297, 346
Writing Skills					
Supporting an Opinion	Grade 7: pp. 57, 59	TE: p. 113 TR: p. 17	TE: p. 221 TR: p. 11	TE: p. 114 TR: 13	SE: pp. 98-99

SE: Student Edition   TE: Teacher's Edition   TR: All-in-One Teaching Resources

World Studies Foundations of Geography	World Studies Latin America	World Studies Medieval Times to Today	World Studies United States and Canada	World Studies Eastern Hemisphere	World Studies Western Hemisphere
TE: p. 35	TE: p. 18 TR: pp. 78, 335	SE: pp. 196-197 TE: pp. 196-197 TR: 389	TE: p. 22 TR: pp. 60, 256, 265	TE: pp. 35, 179, 558, 613	TE: p. 35, 160, 346
SE: pp. 26, 28, 30, 32, 33, 35, 39, 40, 43, 47, 50, 52, 54 TE: pp. 26B, 28, 33, 40, 50 TR: pp. 94, 144, 196, 232, 273	SE: pp. 96, 102, 107, 108, 109, 110, 113, 116, 120, 122 TE: pp. 96B, 102, 109, 116 TR: p. 128	SE: pp. 152, 154, 159, 161, 166, 170, 176, 180, 181, 220, 222, 230, 238 TE: 152b, 154, 161, 170, 180, 220b, 222, 230, 238 TR: 133, 173, 212, 253, 296, 348, 396, 438	SE: pp. 146, 152, 157, 159, 160, 164, 165, 166, 169, 172, 173, 174, 177, 180, 181, 184 TE: pp. 146B, 152, 160, 166, 173, 180 TR: pp. 126, 182, 221, 271, 324	SE: pp. 26, 28, 30, 32, 33, 35, 39, 40, 43, 47, 50, 52, 54, 248, 260, 263, 268, 274, 276, 280, 283, 284, 292, 296, 506, 514, 516, 519, 520, 526, 529, 642, 644, 646, 652, 654, 660, 662, 666, 669, 674, 678, 682	SE: pp. 26, 28, 30, 32, 33, 35, 39, 40, 43, 47, 50, 52, 54, 284, 290, 295, 297, 298, 302, 303, 304, 307, 310, 311, 312, 315, 318, 319, 322, 424, 430, 435, 436, 437, 438, 441, 444, 448, 450
TE: p. 131 TR: p. 9	TE: p. 146 TR: pp. 11, 346	TE: p. 158 TR: pp. 13, 19	TR: pp. 9, 15	TE: p. 146, 236-237, 461, 680	TE: pp. 131, 474 Foundations of Geography TR: p. 9 Latin America TR: pp. 11, 346 United States and Canada TR: pp. 9, 15

SE: Student Edition   TE: Teacher's Edition   TR: All-in-One Teaching Resources

Diagnosing Readiness Correlations (continued)	Test Items	World Studies Africa	World Studies Ancient World	World Studies Asia and the Pacific	World Studies Europe and Russia
Comparing and Contrasting	Grade 7: p. 58	SE: pp. 76, 78, 81, 84, 86, 90–91, 92, 94, 97, 99 TE: pp. 76b, 78, 84, 90–91, 92, 97 TR: 221, 222, 223, 226	SE: pp. 234-235 TE: pp. 234-235 TR: p. 399	SE: pp. 142, 148, 153, 154, 156, 162 TE: 142b, 148, 154, 162 TR: pp. 343-345	SE: pp. 164, 174, 178, 181, 184, 189, 192, 198, 202 TE: pp. 164b, 174, 181, 189, 198 TR: pp. 329, 330, 331
Using a Chart	Grade 6: p. 53	SE: pp. 80, 87, 145, 174, 203 TR: p. 174	SE: pp. 26, 49, 51, 54, 93, 153, 176, 213 TR: p. 255	SE: pp. 22, 79, 187, 193, 233, 236 TR: p. 277	SE: pp. 51, 85, 104, 147, 57 TR: pp. 288, 342
Organizing Information	Grade 6: pp. 53, 54 Grade 7: p. 59	TR: pp. 16, 23	TR: pp. 13, 15, 125, 356, 357, 395-396	TR: pp. 10, 13, 15, 16, 129, 167, 168-169, 274, 283	TR: p. 16

SE: Student Edition   TE: Teacher's Edition   TR: All-in-One Teaching Resources

World Studies Foundations of Geography	World Studies Latin America	World Studies Medieval Times to Today	World Studies United States and Canada	World Studies Eastern Hemisphere	World Studies Western Hemisphere
SE: pp. 58, 60, 62, 66, 67, 68, 71, 74, 76, 79, 80, 81, 84 TE: pp. 44, 58B, 60, 67, 74, 80 TR: pp. 123, 177-179	SE: pp. 140-141, 158, 166, 169, 172, 173, 177, 178, 179, 181, 185, 188, 191, 194 TE: pp. 140-141, 158B, 166, 173, 179, 188 TR: pp. 240, 292, 331-333	SE: pp. 188, 190, 194, 198, 200, 204, 208, 212, 214 TE: pp. 48, 18b, 190, 198, 204, 212 TR: pp. 379, 380, 381	SE: pp. 96, 110, 113, 116, 117, 121, 123, 126, 129, 132, 133, 137, 138 TE: pp. 96B, 110, 117, 126, 133 TR: pp. 251-253	SE: pp. 58, 60, 62, 66, 67, 68, 71, 74, 76, 79, 80, 81, 84, 302, 312, 313, 316, 319, 322, 327, 330, 336, 340, 424, 426, 429, 432, 434, 438-439, 440, 442, 445, 447, 708, 714, 719, 720, 722, 728	SE: pp. 58, 60, 62, 66, 67, 68, 71, 74, 76, 79, 80, 81, 84, 234, 248, 251, 254, 255, 259, 261, 264, 267, 270, 271, 275, 276, 468-469, 486, 494, 497, 500, 501, 505, 506, 507, 509, 513, 516, 519, 522
SE: p. 49	SE: pp. 18, 55, 118 TR: pp. 252, 342	SE: pp. 17, 21, 95, 192, 196, 240	SE: pp. 127, 134, 153, 182 TR: pp. 59, 265, 266, 318	SE: pp. 49, 189, 223, 242, 285, 295, 428, 435, 493, 522, 551, 588, 645, 753, 759, 799, 802	SE: pp. 49, 265, 272, 291, 322, 346, 383, 446, 510
TR: pp. 10, 11, 36, 55, 195	TR: pp. 11, 22, 126-127, 246	TR: pp. 18, 25, 295	TR: pp. 9, 11, 12, 18-21, 73-75, 76-78, 212, 257, 258, 307	Foundations of Geography TR: pp. 10, 11, 36, 55, 195 Europe and Russia TR: p. 16 Africa TR: pp. 16, 23 Asia and the Pacific TR: pp. 10, 13, 15, 16, 129, 167, 168-169, 274, 283	Foundations of Geography TR: pp. 10, 11, 36, 55, 195 Latin America TR: pp. 11, 22, 126-127, 246 United States and Canada TR: pp. 9, 11, 12, 18-21, 73-75, 76-78, 212, 257, 258, 307

SE: Student Edition   TE: Teacher's Edition   TR: All-in-One Teaching Resources

National Geography Standards

The World in Spatial Terms

Standard 1

Use maps and other geographic representations, tools, and technologies to acquire, process, and report information from a spatial perspective.

Standard 2

Use mental maps to organize information about people, places, and environments in a spatial context.

Standard 3

Analyze the spatial organization of people, places, and environments on Earth's surface.

Places and Regions

Standard 4

Understand the physical and human characteristics of places.

Standard 5

Understand that people create regions to interpret Earth's complexity.

Standard 6

Understand how culture and experience influence people's perception of places and regions.

Physical Systems

Standard 7

Understand the physical processes that shape the patterns of Earth's surface.

Standard 8

Understand the characteristics and spatial distribution of ecosystems on Earth's surface.

Human Systems

Standard 9

Understand the characteristics, distribution, and migration of human populations on Earth's surface.

Standard 10

Understand the characteristics, distribution, and complexity of Earth's cultural mosaics.

Standard 11

Understand the patterns and networks of economic interdependence on Earth's surface.

Standard 12

Understand the processes, patterns, and functions of human settlement.

Standard 13

Understand how the forces of cooperation and conflict among people influence division and control of Earth's surface.

Environment and Society

Standard 14

Understand how human actions modify the physical environment.

Standard 15

Understand how physical systems affect human systems.

Standard 16

Understand the changes that occur in the meaning, use, distribution, and importance of resources.

The Uses of Geography

Standard 17

Understand how to apply geography to interpret the past.

Standard 18

Understand how to apply geography to interpret the present and plan for the future.

Foundations of Geography Benchmark Test 1

Directions: *Read each question and choose the best answer. Then mark the letter for the answer you have chosen.*

1. Which of the following lists the themes used to organize information about Earth and its people?

   A. location, animal-plant interaction, movement, position, regions

   B. movement, regions, position, human-environment interaction, place

   C. animal-plant interaction, place, regions, movement, location

   D. location, regions, place, movement, human-environment interaction

Use the global grid and your knowledge of social studies to answer question 2.

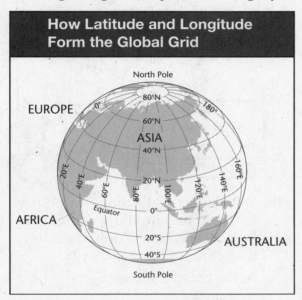

2. According to the global grid, on what continent would you find the address 40°N, 100°E?

   A. Europe

   B. Australia

   C. Africa

   D. Asia

3. What is absolute location?

   A. Absolute location indicates where a place is by describing the places near it.

   B. Absolute location describes the north-south circles around the globe.

   C. Absolute location indicates where a place is by using degrees of latitude and longitude.

   D. Absolute location indicates the absolute degree by identifying its meridian.

4. Which of the following BEST completes this sentence?

   The Rocky Mountains, the Interior Plains, the Nile Valley, and the Coastal Lowlands have unifying characteristics such as climate, land, or history that help define them as

   A. rural locations.

   B. regions.

   C. the American Southwest.

   D. the Prime Meridian.

Foundations of Geography Benchmark Test 1 (continued)

5. When geographers examine the human and physical features at a specific location, they are studying
   A. movement.
   B. space.
   C. place.
   D. human-environment interaction.

6. The most accurate way to show Earth's continents and bodies of water is with a
   A. Mercator projection.
   B. Robinson projection.
   C. globe.
   D. conformal map.

7. All maps include some distortion, or
   A. a loss of color.
   B. a loss of accuracy.
   C. a loss of distance.
   D. a loss of shape.

8. For whom are geographic information systems useful?
   A. geographers, governments, businesses, and mapmakers
   B. mapmakers only
   C. geographers and mapmakers
   D. businesses only

9. What does a geographer determine with a compass rose?
   A. cardinal directions
   B. projection
   C. distance
   D. absolute location

Use the map and your knowledge of social studies to answer question 10.

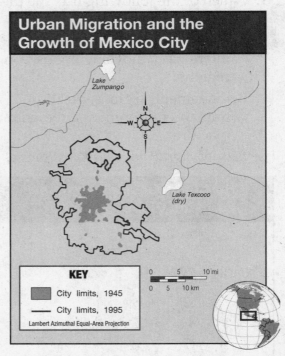

Urban Migration and the Growth of Mexico City

KEY
City limits, 1945
City limits, 1995
Lambert Azimuthal Equal-Area Projection

10. Which part of the map do you need to use to find out how many miles lie between Lake Zumpango and the center of Mexico City?
    A. the compass rose
    B. the key
    C. the title
    D. the scale bar

11. Earth makes one complete rotation on its axis every
    A. month.
    B. day.
    C. year.
    D. two weeks.

Foundations of Geography Benchmark Test 1 *(continued)*

Use the illustration __and__ your knowledge of social studies to answer questions 12–13.

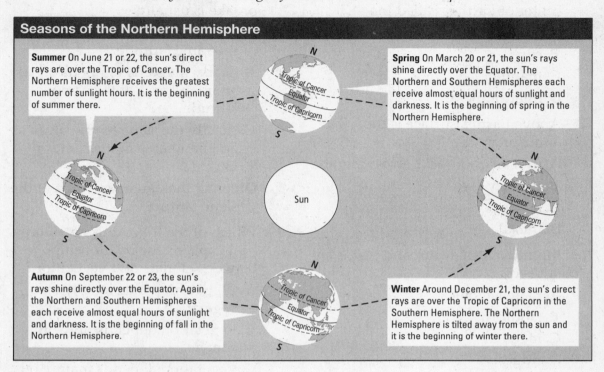

Seasons of the Northern Hemisphere

Summer On June 21 or 22, the sun's direct rays are over the Tropic of Cancer. The Northern Hemisphere receives the greatest number of sunlight hours. It is the beginning of summer there.

Spring On March 20 or 21, the sun's rays shine directly over the Equator. The Northern and Southern Hemispheres each receive almost equal hours of sunlight and darkness. It is the beginning of spring in the Northern Hemisphere.

Sun

Autumn On September 22 or 23, the sun's rays shine directly over the Equator. Again, the Northern and Southern Hemispheres each receive almost equal hours of sunlight and darkness. It is the beginning of fall in the Northern Hemisphere.

Winter Around December 21, the sun's direct rays are over the Tropic of Capricorn in the Southern Hemisphere. The Northern Hemisphere is tilted away from the sun and it is the beginning of winter there.

12. The illustration shows the movement of Earth around the sun. What is the season in the Northern Hemisphere when the sun's direct rays are over the Tropic of Cancer?

A. summer

B. winter

C. fall

D. spring

13. When the Northern Hemisphere is tilted away from the sun, the Southern Hemisphere is titled toward the sun. This explains why the Northern Hemisphere has winter while the Southern Hemisphere has

A. summer.

B. winter.

C. fall.

D. spring.

Foundations of Geography Benchmark Test 1 *(continued)*

14. The sphere of very hot metal at the center of Earth is called the
    A. crust.
    B. core.
    C. mantle.
    D. interior mass.

15. Above Earth's surface is the atmosphere, a
    A. thin layer of rocks and minerals.
    B. cold icy layer.
    C. hot rocky layer.
    D. thick layer of gases.

16. Mountains, plateaus, and plains are types of
    A. plate tectonics.
    B. landforms.
    C. magma.
    D. ridges.

17. In one place, it is hot and sunny one day, and cold and cloudy the next day. The people in that place experienced a change in
    A. climate.
    B. weather.
    C. longitude.
    D. precipitation.

18. In summer, a region near an ocean or lake is usually
    A. warmer than an inland area at the same latitude.
    B. nearly the same temperature as an inland area at the same latitude.
    C. exactly the same temperature as an inland area at the same latitude.
    D. cooler than an inland area at the same latitude.

19. Which of the following statements best explains the relationship between climate and vegetation?
    A. Climate depends mainly on vegetation.
    B. Vegetation depends only on climate.
    C. Vegetation depends mainly on climate.
    D. Climate depends only on vegetation.

20. What kinds of plants grow in the ice pack and pack ice vegetation regions?
    A. grasses and mosses
    B. low shrubs and grasses
    C. deciduous trees
    D. none

Name _____ Class _____ Date_____

Foundations of Geography Benchmark Test 2

Directions: *Read each question and choose the best answer. Then mark the letter for the answer you have chosen.*

1. Demography is the science that studies
   A. where people live and what they do there.
   B. how populations change and why population distribution is uneven.
   C. how people respond to local climates.
   D. when and where people move.

Use the graph and your knowledge of social studies to answer question 2.

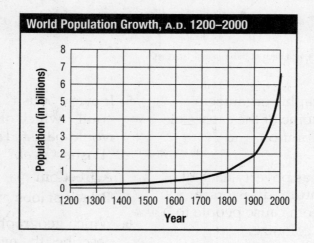

2. The change in population expressed in this graph reflects the result of
   A. the birthrate and death rate being equal.
   B. the failure of the Green Revolution.
   C. the increase of the food supply and improvement in medical care.
   D. the overabundance of fossil fuels.

3. What causes a country's population to grow?
   A. The population density of a specific area grows.
   B. The death rate is higher than the birth rate.
   C. The birth rate is higher than the death rate.
   D. The number of births and the number of deaths are equal.

Name _____ Class _____ Date_____

Foundations of Geography Proficiency Test 2 (continued)

Use the graphic organizers <u>and</u> your knowledge of social studies to answer questions 4-5.

Pushes and Pulls

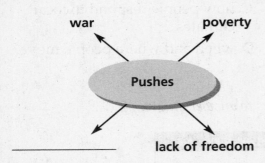

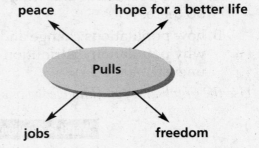

Pushes and pulls are opposites, and each push has a pull "partner."

4. What do the graphic organizers explain about some of the causes of migration, exploration, and colonization?

   A. Things such as poverty, lack of jobs, war, natural disasters, or a lack of freedom cause people to explore and colonize.

   B. Poverty and lack of freedom cause people to stay in one place because life will not be better elsewhere.

   C. People explore and colonize new regions because they want the population to increase.

   D. People are influenced to explore and migrate by the economic opportunities they already have at home.

5. If every "push" has an opposite "pull," which of the following would be listed in the blank on the "Pushes" web?

   A. freedom   **C.** riches

   B. lack of jobs   **D.** fear

6. Which geographic concept best describes the movement from rural to urban areas?

   A. migration loss

   B. immigration

   C. urbanization

   D. population loss

7. What are some effects of more people moving to cities?

   A. People are reacting by moving back to the countryside.

   B. Traffic has gotten much better in some places.

   C. There is an increase in land available for farming.

   D. Cities cannot provide enough services to keep up with the rapid growth.

Foundations of Geography Benchmark Test 2 *(continued)*

8. In developing nations, many people are subsistence farmers, or farmers
   A. who grow soybeans and other legumes.
   B. who raise food and animals for international markets.
   C. who raise food and animals mainly to feed their own families.
   D. who grow food products without using any pesticides.

9. How do businesses hope to benefit from trade alliances such as NAFTA and the European Union?
   A. Businesses hope to increase sales in other countries.
   B. Businesses hope to increase sales in their own countries.
   C. Businesses hope to decrease sales in other countries.
   D. Businesses hope to decrease sales in their own countries.

10. Which form of government involves control by a small group of people?
    A. direct democracy
    B. dictatorship
    C. oligarchy
    D. representative democracy

Use the passage and your knowledge of social studies to answer question 11.

Until about 200 years ago, many countries in the Eastern and Western Hemispheres were absolute monarchies. Most monarchies today are constitutional monarchies. These nations have constitutions.

11. What is the most important difference between an absolute monarchy and a constitutional monarchy?
    A. An absolute monarchy has a king or queen, and a constitutional monarchy does not.
    B. An absolute monarchy does not have a king or queen, but a constitutional monarchy does.
    C. In an absolute monarchy, the king or queen has complete control; in a constitutional monarchy, the king or queen has only limited power.
    D. In an absolute monarchy, the king or queen has only limited power; in a constitutional monarchy, the king or queen has complete control.

12. Early cultures had four major advances in technology. Which happened first?
    A. the invention of tools
    B. the development of civilization
    C. the control of fire
    D. the beginning of agriculture

Foundations of Geography Benchmark Test 2 *(continued)*

13. Which of the following statements best explains the relationship between language and culture?
    A. Language and culture are not related.
    B. Language provides a basis for culture.
    C. Most cultures have language, but a few do not.
    D. A few cultures have language, but most do not.

14. What two factors have recently increased the speed of cultural change, in some ways making the world seem smaller?
    A. the growth of cities and the invention of writing
    B. the invention of tools and the beginnings of agriculture
    C. the growth of industry and the spread of factories in America
    D. advances in both transportation and communication technology

15. What are the two main groups of natural resources?
    A. living resources and nonrenewable resources
    B. recyclable resources and renewable resources
    C. renewable resources and recyclable resources
    D. renewable resources and nonrenewable resources

16. Which of the following is a fossil fuel?
    A. petroleum
    B. electricity
    C. biomass
    D. wind

17. What term do geographers use to identify peoples' natural surroundings?
    A. resources
    B. environment
    C. industrialization
    D. energy sources

18. Which of the following is a first-level economic activity?
    A. banking
    B. spinning wool
    C. farming
    D. selling groceries

19. Which of the following causes deforestation?
    A. air pollution
    B. cutting down too many trees
    C. planting too many trees
    D. water pollution

20. An example of service activities impacting the environment is
    A. the construction of roads, telephone lines, and power lines.
    B. the additional employment opportunities created.
    C. increased prosperity.
    D. decreased prosperity.

The United States and Canada
Benchmark Test 1

Directions: *Read each question and choose the best answer. Then mark the letter for the answer you have chosen.*

1. What is one way in which bodies of water have affected life in the United States and Canada?

   A. The presence of lakes and rivers has stopped people from moving between regions in both countries.

   B. Large rivers cannot be used for transportation because they are too difficult to navigate.

   C. The presence of lakes and rivers has helped industry to develop in the two countries.

   D. The United States and Canada use their large rivers as a border between the two countries.

2. How are the United States and Canada most likely to act in the future to protect the Great Lakes?

   A. The United States will act on its own, because the lakes are mostly in the United States.

   B. Canada will act on its own, because the lakes are mostly in Canada.

   C. Canada will protect the three largest lakes, and the United States will protect the two smaller lakes.

   D. The United States and Canada will work together, because four of the five lakes lie on the border between the two countries.

3. Why are grasslands, or prairies, important in the United States and Canada?

   A. They are the areas where logging is most successful.

   B. They are the areas where wheat and other food crops are grown.

   C. They are the areas that contain permafrost.

   D. They are the areas that have the richest mineral deposits.

4. Which statement best describes the distribution of natural resources in the United States and Canada?

   A. The United States has more land that is suitable for farming than Canada.

   B. The United States has little fresh water, while Canada has plenty.

   C. Canada has more land that is suitable for farming than the United States.

   D. Canada imports fresh water from the United States.

The United States and Canada Benchmark Test 1 (continued)

Use the graph <u>and</u> your knowledge of social studies to answer question 5.

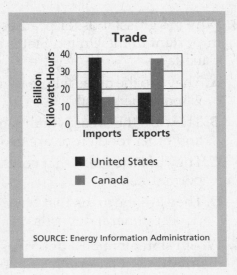

SOURCE: Energy Information Administration

5. Which statement is supported by information in the graph?
   A. Both the United States and Canada import more electric power than they export.
   B. Both the United States and Canada export more electric power than they import.
   C. The United States is more dependent on imported electric power than Canada is.
   D. Canada is more dependent on imported electric power than the United States is.

6. Thomas Jefferson supported the independence of the colonies from British rule by writing the
   A. Mayflower Compact.
   B. English Bill of Rights.
   C. Declaration of Independence.
   D. Magna Carta.

7. What impact did the arrival of Europeans have on Native Americans in North America?
   A. Native Americans became rich from the wealth of trading opportunities that came with the arrival of the settlers.
   B. Colonists often enslaved Native Americans, and missionaries tried to convert them to their religion.
   C. Missionaries converted all the Native Americans to Catholicism and taught them to read and write.
   D. A bitter rivalry developed between northern and southern Native Americans over which group would trade with the colonists.

Use the passage <u>and</u> your knowledge of social studies to answer question 8.

> There were several reasons the United States wanted California to become part of the United States. One important reason was that many Americans saw their nation and its democratic government as the best in the world. They believed that Americans had the right and the duty to spread their culture across the continent all the way to the Pacific Ocean.

8. The passage describes the concept
   A. of Manifest Destiny.
   B. of the forty-niners.
   C. of Sutter's Mill.
   D. of the Gold Rush.

The United States and Canada Proficiency Test 1 (continued)

Use the timeline and your knowledge of social studies to answer questions 9-11.

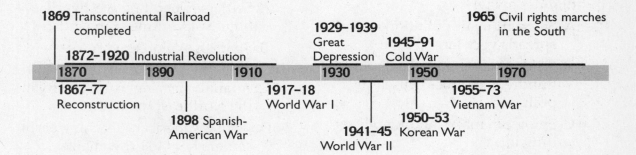

9. Which of the following is the earliest event listed on the timeline?
   A. Industrial Revolution
   B. Vietnam War
   C. Cold War
   D. Reconstruction

10. After World War I, the United States' economy
   A. fell into disaster, but then recovered in 1929.
   B. boomed, but then fell into disaster in 1929.
   C. boomed and stayed strong until the beginning of World War II.
   D. immediately fell into disaster and didn't recover until the beginning of World War II.

11. What other event occurred during the period of the Cold War?
   A. World War I
   B. Spanish American War
   C. Korean War
   D. Great Depression

12. What is one effect that industrialization had on life in the United States and Canada?
   A. People in both nations benefited from the trade of goods and services.
   B. The environment of Lake Erie remained pollution-free.
   C. New spinning machines and power looms slowed down cloth-making.
   D. The lives of only a few people in each country were changed by industrialization.

13. During World War II, what happened just after Germany's ally, Japan, attacked the United States naval base at Pearl Harbor, Hawaii?
   A. The United States declared war on Japan, and Germany declared war on the United States.
   B. The United States declared war on both Japan and Germany.
   C. The United States declared war on Japan, Germany, and Russia.
   D. Japan refused to acknowledge the United States' declaration of war.

The United States and Canada Proficiency Test 1 (continued)

14. What effect can air pollution in large cities have on areas hundreds of miles away?

   A. Smog from air pollution never spreads very far.

   B. Acid rain carried to cities across hundreds of miles causes air pollution.

   C. Smog can make landing planes difficult.

   D. Air pollutants lead to acid rain, which the wind carries long distances.

15. Who is the head of the Canadian government?

   A. the British monarch

   B. the Canadian senator

   C. the Canadian prime minister

   D. the British prime minister

16. In 1969, a huge fire caused by a thick layer of pollutants burned on top of the Cuyahoga River. How did the fire affect the relationship between the United States and Canada?

   A. Canada refused to use drinking water sent from the United States.

   B. The United States and Canada signed a treaty promising to cooperate in cleaning up Lake Erie.

   C. Canada charged the United States with violating the Clean Water Treaty.

   D. The United States accused Canada of allowing its factories to pollute United States waterways.

17. Which of the following statements is an example of a *cultural exchange*?

   A. Settlers expanding westward onto Native American lands.

   B. Spanish explorers circumnavigating the globe.

   C. A family moving from one city in the Northeast to another.

   D. Native Americans teaching early settlers how to grow maize.

18. Although jazz is a uniquely American form of music,

   A. it began in Great Britain with Louis Armstrong.

   B. it represents the South American rhythms.

   C. it has its roots in African rhythms.

   D. it was actually created in Canada by the Group of Seven.

19. One way Canadians have preserved their French heritage is

   A. by passing laws that promote French culture and language.

   B. by setting strict limits on immigration.

   C. by allowing indigenous people to live on reserves.

   D. by granting Inuits land in parts of the Northwest Territory.

20. Inuit tribes in the arctic regions of Canada are able to survive because

   A. their hunting and craftworking skills allow them to make everything they need to survive.

   B. modern technology allows them to buy special clothes and tools.

   C. they only live in the arctic during the summer.

   D. they are able to stock up on supplies on their rare visits to the cities.

The United States and Canada
Benchmark Test 2

Directions: *Read each question and choose the best answer. Then mark the letter for the answer you have chosen.*

1. Why was Ellis Island important to the millions of immigrants who came to the United States between 1892 and 1954?

   A. It was the only port of entry for immigrants.

   B. It offered inexpensive farmland to immigrants .

   C. It was the main port of entry for immigrants.

   D. It offered excellent job opportunities to immigrants.

2. An important change in the economy of the South during the past half century was a shift

   A. from an economy based on agriculture to one based on textiles.

   B. from an economy based on agriculture to one based on industry.

   C. from an economy based on textiles to one based on tourism.

   D. from an economy based on industry to one based on tourism.

3. Imagine a map of the United States, color coded to show population density. If the color orange shows the greatest population density, which region of the country has the most orange?

   A. the Northeast   C. the Midwest

   B. the South   D. the West

Use the graph __and__ your knowledge of social studies to answer question 4.

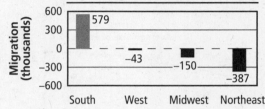

African American Migration by Region, 1990–2000

SOURCE: Population Reference Bureau

4. What does the graph show about the migration of African Americans within the United States?

   A. From 1990 to 2000 more African Americans lived in the South than in any other region of the country.

   B. From 1990 to 2000 African Americans moved away from the South and into the other three regions of the country.

   C. From 1990 to 2000 African Americans moved away from the South and the Northeast and into the West and the Midwest.

   D. From 1990 to 2000 African Americans moved into the South and away from the other three regions of the country.

The United States and Canada Benchmark Test 2 *(continued)*

Use the graphs <u>and</u> your knowledge of social studies to answer question 5.

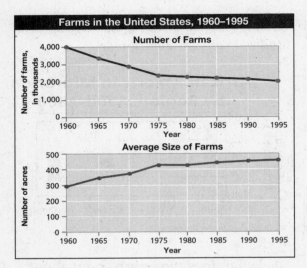

Farms in the United States, 1960–1995

5. What conclusion can be drawn from these graphs?

   A. Between 1960 and 1995 there was an increase in size and number of farms.

   B. Between 1960 and 1995 there was a decrease in size and number of farms.

   C. Between 1960 and 1995 there was an increase in number and a decrease in size of farms.

   D. Between 1960 and 1995 there was a decrease in number and an increase in size of farms.

6. During the 1980s the demand for farm products decreased because the country went through a recession, which is

   A. an upturn in business activity.

   B. a downturn in business activity.

   C. a decrease in annual rainfall.

   D. an increase in annual rainfall.

7. Who were the first people to live in the West of the United States?

   A. Pilgrims

   B. Spanish settlers

   C. Native Americans

   D. Spanish missionaries

8. What happened to the miners and prospectors who went to California for the Gold Rush?

   A. Most found gold and returned home wealthy.

   B. Most never found any gold and returned home with less money than they had before leaving.

   C. About half found gold and stayed in California, while the other half did not find gold and returned home.

   D. Most did not find gold, but many stayed in California.

9. What has made Toronto a major trade and transportation center?

   A. It was founded in 1793.

   B. It is located on Lake Ontario.

   C. Nearly half its residents are foreign-born.

   D. It was first known as York.

The United States and Canada Proficiency Test 2 (*continued*)

Use the graph __and__ your knowledge of social studies to answer question 10.

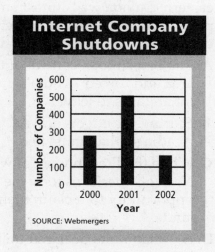

Internet Company Shutdowns

Number of Companies

600
500
400
300
200
100
0

2000   2001   2002
Year

SOURCE: Webmergers

10. During the 1990s thousands of internet companies started up, mostly in the West. What does the graph tell about what happened during the first years of the twenty-first century?

A. Fewer internet companies started up during that time.

B. The growth of internet companies doubled during that time.

C. Some internet companies started up during that time, and others closed.

D. Nearly a thousand internet companies closed during that time.

11. Today the majority of Quebec's population is made up of

A. French citizens.

B. immigrants.

C. United States citizens.

D. Francophones.

12. Which region of the United States is most similar to the Prairie Provinces of Canada?

A. the Northeast

B. the South

C. the Midwest

D. the West

13. What major geographic feature separates British Columbia from the rest of Canada?

A. the Rocky Mountains

B. the Atlantic Ocean

C. the St. Lawrence River

D. Hudson Bay

14. Why did the Canadian government put a partial ban on cod fishing in 1992?

A. There were too many cod off the coast of the Atlantic Provinces.

B. The waters off the coast of the Atlantic Provinces had been overfished.

C. The government promised to give other countries an opportunity to fish for cod.

D. The cod off the coast of the Atlantic Provinces had been poisoned.

15. In Nunavut about 85 percent of the population are

A. Inuit.

B. of European descent.

C. of Asian descent.

D. Dene.

16. What caused the huge number of buffalo herds to disappear in the Prairie Provinces of Canada?

    A. Native Americans acquired horses and were able to hunt more effectively.

    B. Native Americans began to hunt for sport and hides.

    C. People of European descent moved into the region and hunted buffalo mainly for sport and hides.

    D. Disease killed most of the young buffalo, and they were not able to reproduce.

17. Which of the following statements describes the treatment of Native Americans in British Columbia during and after the gold rush?

    A. Native people went from being a small percentage of the population before the gold rush to being a large percentage after it.

    B. Settlers who had just arrived for the gold rush took over Native American land and forced native people onto small reserves.

    C. Native children were not required to attend government schools.

    D. Native Americans continued to practice their own customs, religions, and languages undisturbed.

18. Before the Seven Year War between Britain and France, Acadia in eastern Canada was almost entirely populated by people of French descent. What caused it to change?

    A. The British took control of the area and forced Acadia's inhabitants to leave.

    B. Fearing the effects of war, Acadia's inhabitants fled.

    C. While the French were at war, Native Americans took the opportunity to reclaim their land.

    D. Its inhabitants declared their loyalty to Britain and renounced their French ancestry.

19. The Atlantic Provinces of Canada have a long history in the fishing and shipbuilding industries. What is a more recent industry for the area?

    A. aquaculture, or fish-farming

    B. maritime tourism

    C. modern boat design

    D. ocean fishing

20. Members of the House of Commons, a part of the Canadian Parliament, represent

    A. Territories, but not Provinces.

    B. both Territories and Provinces, but with more control over the Territories.

    C. both the Territories and the Provinces, but with more control over the Provinces.

    D. neither the Territories or the Provinces.

Latin America Benchmark Test 1

Directions: *Read each question and choose the best answer. Then mark the letter for the answer you have chosen.*

1. The Caribbean is east of
   A. Latin America.
   B. Middle America.
   C. North America.
   D. South America.

2. Which of the following is located in Latin America?
   A. the Gobi Desert
   B. the Sahara
   C. the Rocky Mountains
   D. the Andes Mountains

3. The isthmus of Central America connects
   A. Mexico and South America.
   B. the Pacific and Atlantic Oceans.
   C. South America to North America.
   D. Mexico to the Caribbean.

4. A hurricane in the Caribbean might have an effect on the economy in the United States by
   A. increasing the price of bananas in the market.
   B. lowering the price of bananas in the market.
   C. increasing the amount of bananas in the United States.
   D. increasing the amount of bananas grown in the Caribbean.

5. Depending on the export of one cash crop or natural resource is risky for nations in Latin America because
   A. their supply of natural resources will be exhausted in the next ten years.
   B. the country might make too much money.
   C. if something were to happen to hurt the value of the crop or resource, the country's economy could go into crisis.
   D. most countries in the world are not buying crops or natural resources exported from other countries.

Use the chart <u>and</u> your knowledge of social studies to answer question 6.

Region	Type	Example
Mexico and Central America	Riches of land and sea	minerals: silver, gold, copper, oil, natural gas, forests, rich soil, fish
The Caribbean	Farming and mineral resources	rich soil, minerals: bauxite, nickel, oil
South America	A wealth of resources	minerals, including oil forests fish rich soil

6. Mexico and Venezuela have large supplies of what resource?
   A. nickel   C. bauxite
   B. natural gas   D. oil

Latin America Benchmark Test 1 (continued)

Use the map <u>and</u> your knowledge of social studies to answer questions 7-8.

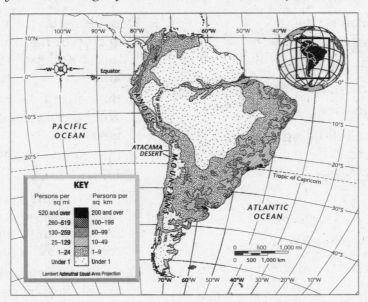

7. Where are the most densely populated areas in South America?

  A. along the Amazon River

  B. in the Andes mountains

  C. inland

  D. along the coasts

8. Why are most densely populated areas located where they are?

  A. It is too cold to live inland in South America.

  B. The rain forest and the plains are prime places for large cities.

  C. Ports are important in trade, and water sources provide energy and other natural resources.

  D. Mountainous regions attract farming and fishing industries.

9. How might having and using natural resources affect the economies of Latin American nations and nations such as the United States?

  A. Having natural resources makes countries dependent on other countries for secondary industries.

  B. Having natural resources allows countries the opportunity to prosper by producing products for their own needs and for export.

  C. Having natural resources makes countries responsible for protecting nature and wildlife habitats.

  D. Having natural resources guarantees a thriving economy.

Latin America Benchmark Test 1 *(continued)*

10. About A.D. 900, the _____ suddenly left their cities.

    A. Mayans

    B. Aztecs

    C. Incans

    D. Mayans and the Incans both

11. How do the Quechua preserve Incan culture?

    A. by using the Incan language and practicing traditions such as spinning wool and weaving.

    B. by continuing to worship the Incan gods and practicing human sacrifice.

    C. by continuing to live in Machu Picchu, a city that has changed very little in the last 500 years.

    D. Incan culture has not been preserved.

12. The Europeans who colonized the region of Latin America from the 1500s onward were primarily from

    A. Spain.

    B. Portugal.

    C. the Aztec Empire.

    D. England.

Use the time line and your knowledge of social studies to answer questions 13-14.

1770s–1780s	Revolutions that will inspire Haiti's leaders occur in North America and France.
1794–1804	Followers of Toussaint L'Ouverture fight for and win Haiti's independence.
1804–1825	Troops led by Simón Bolívar free several countries from Spanish rule.
1810–1821	Miguel Hidalgo begins the struggle for Mexican independence. Agustín de Iturbide fights Spain and ultimately declares Mexico independent.
1817–1821	José de San Martín leads Argentina and Chile in the fight for freedom.
1822	Dom Pedro, Portuguese ruler of Brazil, declares the colony independent.

13. How did the American and French revolutions affect the fight for Latin American independence?

    A. Simón Bolívar learned to fight in them and then became a military leader in Latin America.

    B. Mexico was freed from Spain during the American Revolution.

    C. They inspired Haitian leaders to fight for independence.

    D. They forced Dom Pedro to declare Brazil independent.

14. How did Brazil's route to freedom differ from that of other countries in Latin America?

    A. Brazil simply declared independence, whereas the other countries had to fight.

    B. Brazil fought for the shortest amount of time.

    C. Brazil fought for the longest time.

    D. Brazilians had to fight whereas other countries simply declared themselves independent.

Latin America Benchmark Test 1 (continued)

15. What was the "Cry of Dolores?"

    A. the desire for independence across Latin America

    B. Hidalgo's call for revolution and Mexican independence

    C. the way Mexicans traditionally called family members to dinner

    D. San Martín's call for revolution and Argentinean independence

16. Indigenous people in the Americas are descendants of

    A. Spaniards.

    B. Europeans.

    C. the people who first lived in the region.

    D. both Europeans and Native Americans.

17. Which of the following is a factor that led to ethnic variety in the Caribbean?

    A. Many inhabitants came as colonists, slaves, or immigrants.

    B. The wide variety of religious beliefs has created a diverse culture.

    C. Internal political struggles continually erupt in the governments of the Caribbean.

    D. Gold discovered in the area lured many from around the world.

18. Which of the following is a definition for the term *ethnic group*?

    A. people who share a language, history, and culture

    B. people who trade ideas and customs with one another

    C. parents, children, grandparents, aunts, uncles, and other relatives living together

    D. an area in which people share the same cultural traits

19. Why do the countries of South America have to import food to eat?

    A. The land of South America is too dry to farm a large quantity of crops.

    B. The only land used for farming in South America is owned by subsistence farmers.

    C. Export farming uses so much land for cash crops that South America has to import food to eat.

    D. The population of South America is booming, and the farmers cannot produce enough crops to feed all the people.

20. Gauchos, who work on Argentina's pampas, or grasslands, are

    A. ladinos.

    B. farmers.

    C. plantation owners.

    D. cowboys.

Latin America Benchmark Test 2

Directions: *Read each question and choose the best answer. Then mark the letter for the answer you have chosen.*

1. In Mexico, how is city life different from life in the rural villages?

   A. Life is difficult for the poor in both villages and cities, but the cities offer every family public housing.

   B. Life is difficult for the poor in both villages and cities, but the cities offer children of poor families a better education.

   C. Life is much better in the cities because people don't have to work as hard.

   D. Life is much better in the villages because there are plenty of good paying jobs.

Use the picture and your knowledge of social studies to answer question 2.

Mexico City

Smog (pollution)

2. Why is there less smog on the north side of Mexico City?

   A. because there are more factories on the north side of Mexico City

   B. because the wind in Mexico always travels from northwest to southeast

   C. because the mountainous areas have less vegetation and cannot absorb the pollution as well as the greener north side

   D. because the mountainous areas to the east, south, and west of the city trap the pollution in the bowl shaped valley

Latin America Proficiency Test 2 (continued)

Use the chart and your knowledge of social studies to answer question 3.

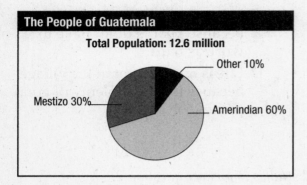

The People of Guatemala

Total Population: 12.6 million

Other 10%

Mestizo 30%

Amerindian 60%

3. Approximately how many Native Americans live in Guatemala?
   A. 1.2 million   C. 7.6 million
   B. 3.8 million   D. 10 million

4. People in Guatemala who are descendents of Native Americans and Spaniards who came to the area are known as
   A. Yanomami.   C. Incas.
   B. Creoles.   D. ladinos.

5. Which country houses a major transportation corridor from the Atlantic to the Pacific oceans?
   A. Panama   C. Guatemala
   B. Honduras   D. Haiti

6. What did engineers have to design in order to make the Panama Canal possible?
   A. a railroad
   B. a system of locks
   C. steam powered equipment
   D. a seven-foot-wide road

7. How did the United States and its desire for a shortcut between oceans change Panama's history?
   A. The United States helped Panama win its independence from Colombia in order to build the Panama Canal.
   B. The United States paid a French company to build the Panama Canal.
   C. The United States refused to trade with Panama after they built the Panama Canal.
   D. The United States helped Panama win its independence from Spain in order to build the Panama Canal.

8. From which country did Cuba gain its independence in 1898?
   A. Spain   B. Portugal
   C. America   D. Great Britain

9. Which of the following is true of Fidel Castro's government?
   A. It has freedom of press.
   B. It owns little of the country's land.
   C. It is Communist.
   D. Most businesses are private.

10. Based on his actions and goals, what kind of government did Toussaint L'Ouverture most likely envision for Haiti?
    A. military rule
    B. democracy
    C. dictatorship
    D. colonial government

Latin America Benchmark Test 2 *(continued)*

11. The farmers of Haiti struggle to make a living. Why?

   A. Most trees have been cut down, causing topsoil to wash away.

   B. The government restricts the size of farms.

   C. There is not enough rainfall and no system of irrigation.

   D. The farmers do not have access to modern farming technology.

12. Haiti lies on the western third of which island?

   A. Puerto Rico

   B. Hispaniola

   C. Jamaica

   D. Honduras

13. Which of the following statements describes the relationship between Puerto Rico and the United States?

   A. Puerto Rico is a state of the United States.

   B. Puerto Rico is an independent country.

   C. Puerto Rico is a colony of the United States.

   D. Puerto Rico is a commonwealth of the United States.

14. A tourist visiting San Juan today would find

   A. that Spain has been Puerto Rico's only influence for the past 500 years.

   B. that Puerto Rican cities are mainly influenced by other islands in the Caribbean and no longer Spain.

   C. that Puerto Rican cities show influences of Spanish, Caribbean, and Unites States mainland culture.

   D. that the United States mainland culture is the only influence that remains in Puerto Rico.

15. Many people created cities along rivers in the United States during the eighteenth and nineteenth centuries. However, along the Amazon, there are only a few cities with a middle-to-high population. Why is this so?

   A. The rain forest makes it difficult for people to travel and live along the Amazon.

   B. Building along the Amazon is restricted by the government.

   C. The Amazon runs through a desert.

   D. The pollution in the Amazon poses dangers to residents' health.

Latin America Benchmark Test 2 *(continued)*

16. The capital of Brazil was moved from the coast to the interior because the government wished to

    A. develop the interior region using the resources of the rain forest.

    B. provide services to people living in the rain forest.

    C. move from the flooding and heavy rains that plagued the coast.

    D. move the capital to where more people already lived.

17. What happened to the isolated indigenous people of the Amazon's rain forest when Brazil opened the region for development?

    A. They ignored development and continued as they were.

    B. Many were killed by disease and violence.

    C. They decided to move to the cities.

    D. Many bought land from the government to protect their homes.

18. What are the three major geographic regions of Peru?

    1. a cold mountainous region, or sierra.

    2. a large interior plain, or savanna.

    3. a coastal desert scattered with oases.

    4. a large rain forest, or selva.

    A. 1, 2 and 3

    B. 2, 3 and 4

    C. 1, 2 and 4

    D. 1, 3 and 4

19. What factors have helped Chile create a billion-dollar agricultural industry?

    1. When it is summer in Chile, it is winter in the United States, Europe, and Japan.

    2. Because of the Andes, Chilean fruit is naturally pest free.

    3. Chile has year-round summer.

    4. Chilean scientists have created an "all natural" pesticide.

    A. both 1 and 4

    B. both 3 and 4

    C. both 2 and 3

    D. both 1 and 2

20. After oil prices dropped in the mid-1980s, Venezuela's government decided to

    A. pour more money into oil production.

    B. take over privately owned businesses.

    C. sell its industries to private companies.

    D. invest in building subways and highways.

Europe and Russia Benchmark Test 1

Directions: *Read each question and choose the best answer. Then mark the letter for the answer you have chosen.*

1. Which of the following describes the continent of Europe?
   A. It is an island surrounded by oceans and seas on all sides.
   B. It was created by volcanoes which erupted millions of years ago.
   C. It is a peninsula which juts out into the Atlantic Ocean and has many smaller peninsulas.
   D. It is the second largest continent.

2. The Ural Mountains form
   A. a natural barrier between Spain and France.
   B. the dividing line between Europe and Asia.
   C. a protective barrier for Russia from cold north winds.
   D. the eastern boundary of Siberia.

3. The largest plain in the world is located in
   A. Siberia.
   B. the Balkans.
   C. Eastern Europe.
   D. north central Europe.

4. The northern areas of Russia are covered by
   A. lakes which provide ports for shipping.
   B. Mediterranean vegetation such as fruit and olive trees.
   C. rainforests which are hot and humid all year.
   D. tundra which can't be used for farming.

5. Which of the following describes the government of ancient Greece?
   A. It was ruled by an emperor who was an absolute monarch.
   B. It had many city-states and many were democracies.
   C. Athens controlled the government of all the city-states.
   D. All people were considered citizens and could vote, including women and slaves.

6. One great accomplishment of the Roman Empire was
   A. a system of hard-surfaced roads which all led to Rome.
   B. a system of underground palaces and churches.
   C. the invention and use of the wheel.
   D. a university where the first scientists studied plants and animals.

7. In 27 B.C., the first emperor of Rome, Augustus, took control. This began
   A. Rule Romana, or Roman rule that lasted for 200 years.
   B. Pax Romana, or a series of failed invasions.
   C. Pax Romana, or Roman peace that lasted for 200 years.
   D. Peace Romero, or Roman civil war that lasted for a decade.

Europe and Russia Benchmark Test 1 (continued)

Use the map __and__ your knowledge of social studies to answer questions 8-9.

Europe and Russia: Natural Resources

8. Based on the map, where are the majority of natural resources located in Europe and Russia?

   A. only in Western Europe

   B. along the Mediterranean Sea

   C. in Eastern Europe and some parts of Russia

   D. near the Arctic Circle

9. What main forms of natural resources are located in the United Kingdom?

   A. bauxite and lead

   B. coal and lead

   C. hydroelectric power and iron

   D. coal and hydroelectric power

10. Which countries had revolutions in the 1600s and 1700s which helped lead to limits on the power of absolute monarchs?

   A. England and France

   B. England and Spain

   C. Russia and France

   D. Russia and Germany

11. Which was the first industry affected by the Industrial Revolution?

   A. the shipping industry of Spain

   B. the food manufacturing industry of France

   C. the textile industry of Great Britain

   D. the mining industry of Germany

Europe and Russia Proficiency Test 1 (continued)

Use the timeline <u>and</u> your knowledge of social studies to answer questions 12–14.

1613	Romanovs take power
1689	Peter the Great takes throne; westernization begins
1762	Catherine the Great takes power; westernization continues
1905	Russian Duma established
1917	Last of the Romanovs, Nicholas II, is forced from power; Lenin begins Communist government
1922	Lenin and Communists win civil war
1924	Stalin takes over after Lenin's death
1945	World War II ends and the Cold War begins
1985	Gorbachev comes to power and allows more freedoms
1991	Communism ends; Soviet Union becomes the Russian Federation and other independent nations

12. About how long did the Romanov family rule Russia?

A. about 100 years

B. about 200 years

C. about 300 years

D. about 50 years

13. Which leaders tried to westernize Russia?

A. Peter the Great and Catherine the Great

B. Lenin and Stalin

C. Peter the Great and Nicholas II

D. Catherine the Great and Stalin

14. What event ended the Cold War?

A. Gorbachev coming to power in 1985

B. the end of Communism in Russia in 1991

C. nuclear testing by the United States and Russia in 1962

D. the beginning of the European Economic Community in 1957

Europe and Russia Benchmark Test 1 (continued)

15. The European Union establishes policies for many things including
   A. health care and national defense.
   B. national defense and education.
   C. education and international trade.
   D. programs that promote North American heritage studies.

16. Which of the following describes the movements of people within Europe since the Industrial Revolution?
   A. Fewer people were needed for farming; they moved to cities to work in factories.
   B. More people were needed for farming; people moved to the country to work on farms.
   C. People moved from the south to the north because new houses could be kept warmer.
   D. People moved away from the seacoasts to areas which were richer in natural resources.

17. Prague and Budapest are examples of
   A. how communism permanently hindered cultural development of cities.
   B. the life and culture found in Eastern European cities.
   C. cities that have rejected their European heritage.
   D. the life and culture found in Western European cities.

18. Creating works of art has been a tradition among the Russians. One famous Russian cultural symbol is
   A. Vaclav Havel.
   B. Wolfgang Mozart.
   C. Vladivostok.
   D. St. Petersburg.

19. Which country was the site of the Velvet Revolution in 1989?
   A. Germany
   B. Russia
   C. Yugoslavia
   D. Czechoslovakia

20. How do Europe's fast trains affect the culture of the region?
   A. They are helping to relieve the traffic in many of Europe's big cities.
   B. They make travel between countries easier and allow more cross-cultural contact.
   C. They are becoming so popular they may replace airplanes for travel within Europe.
   D. Fast trains are convenient for travel, but have no effect on Europe's cultures.

Name _____ Class _____ Date_____

Europe and Russia Proficiency Test 2

Directions: *Read each question and choose the best answer. Then mark the letter for the answer you have chosen.*

Use the chart and your knowledge of social studies to answer questions 1-2.

800s	Kingdom of Wessex unifies England into a nation
1215	King John forced to sign Magna Carta which requires him to obey laws of the land; nobles later become Parliament
1500s	Wales officially becomes part of English nation; England begins to build a large empire
1700s	England and Scotland joined together
1801	Act of Union formally brings Ireland under control of Great Britain
Mid-1800s	"The sun never sets on the British Empire" because it is so large

1. Which statement is supported by the information in the chart?
   A. The British empire grew over hundreds of years.
   B. Northern Ireland became part of the United Kingdom but Southern Ireland didn't.
   C. Adding Wales did not help England build its empire.
   D. The Magna Carta required nobles to become Parliament.

2. Which event was important in adding colonies to the British Empire?
   A. The American Revolution in 1776
   B. Great Britain helps defeat Napoleon in 1815
   C. The Act of Union in 1801
   D. The Magna Carta in 1215

3. British Parliament is made up of
   A. representatives appointed by the reigning monarch.
   B. a single house: the House of Commons.
   C. two houses: the House of Lords and the House of Commons.
   D. a group of nobles called the House of Lords.

4. One indication of the pride the French have had in their culture is
   A. their refusal to join the European Union.
   B. their support for schools speaking native languages in their colonies in the 1900s.
   C. their support for immigration throughout the 1900s.
   D. the Academy, which has preserved the French language since the 1600s.

Europe and Russia Benchmark Test 2 *(continued)*

5. After World War II, Algerian and other immigrants came to France and
   A. continued to speak only their first languages.
   B. decided to stay and make their homes there.
   C. returned home once they had saved enough money.
   D. became very important in French literature and arts.

6. Which of the following are reasons that Sweden had a very large national debt in the late 1980s?
   A. The economy was slow but the government was still paying large benefits to citizens.
   B. It had borrowed money to upgrade its factories.
   C. Communism prevented Sweden from trading with many of its neighbors.
   D. The farming and forestry industries were hurt by too much pollution.

7. One way Sweden can improve its economy and still keep its welfare system is by
   A. limiting fishing rights for other countries along its coast.
   B. seeking foreign investment in nuclear power plants.
   C. concentrating on service industries like banking and finance.
   D. making better use of its natural resources and making its factories more efficient.

8. Vatican City is world headquarters for
   A. many multinational corporations.
   B. the Roman Catholic Church.
   C. the fashion industry.
   D. NATO.

9. For the first time in the late 1800s, Italy was
   A. divided into separate countries in the north and south.
   B. attacked by invaders from the south.
   C. united as a single country.
   D. accepted as an ally of the United States.

10. After World War II, Italy tried to improve the economy in the south by
   A. encouraging foreign investment in new factories.
   B. instituting land reform which allowed more people to own land.
   C. reducing taxes to promote investment.
   D. moving its capital there to promote trade and travel.

Europe and Russia Benchmark Test 2 (continued)

11. Germany became East Germany and West Germany
   A. after World War I and Hitler promised to reunite them.
   B. because the two areas spoke different languages and had different cultures.
   C. when the two areas fought a civil war just after World War II.
   D. after World War II and was a symbol of the Cold War.

12. Control of the government in Poland has changed many times in its history. After World War II
   A. the Soviet Union took control.
   B. it finally became independent.
   C. it joined the European Union.
   D. it was controlled by East Germany.

13. Which of the following best describes farms in Poland?
   A. Most are small and may not be large enough for a farmer to earn a living.
   B. Most are large collectives which supply much of Europe with food.
   C. Most are still owned by the government and need new machinery.
   D. There are very few farms in Poland because the soil is poor.

14. How did the new Macedonian constitution try to calm tensions between ethnic Macedonians and ethnic Albanians?
   A. It removed language that had made Macedonians second-class citizens.
   B. It contained an addition that guaranteed Macedonians special rights.
   C. It removed language that had made Albanians second-class citizens.
   D. It contained an addition that guaranteed Albanians special rights.

15. What caused the breakup of the former Yugoslavia?
   A. At the end of WWII, it joined the U.S.S.R. and was no longer its own independent nation.
   B. At the end of the Cold War, peace treaties were signed that forced Yugoslavia to disband.
   C. Tensions between different ethnic groups worsened until civil war erupted.
   D. After the fall of Communism, the various republics that formed Yugoslavia peacefully declared independence.

Europe and Russia Benchmark Test 2 (continued)

16. Economic sanctions were used by many countries against which of the following in the 1990s?
    A. Macedonia
    B. Yugoslavia
    C. Turkey
    D. Ukraine

17. Why has Ukraine attracted so many invaders over the years?
    A. because of its location between Europe and Russia and its abundance of natural resources
    B. because it has refused to cooperate with its neighbors
    C. because its religion is different than its neighbors' religion
    D. because it has continually tried to conquer other nations

18. Chernobyl is a well-known name because
    A. it is home to the Bolshoi Ballet.
    B. it rebelled against Russia in a civil war.
    C. it is the first stop on the Trans-Siberian Railroad.
    D. it is the site of a nuclear accident that killed many people and poisoned the land and water.

19. In the first years of capitalism in Russia
    A. the people of Moscow gave up their traditional ways.
    B. the government cracked down on corruption.
    C. some investors became very wealthy.
    D. medical care was greatly improved and made more affordable.

20. During the 1990s, many Russians lost their life savings because
    A. they invested in the stock market before it crashed.
    B. the banks failed and inflation was very high.
    C. the government raised taxes to pay for social programs.
    D. a severe drought created a financial crisis.

Africa Benchmark Test 1

Directions: *Read each question and choose the best answer. Then mark the letter for the answer you have chosen.*

1. Which kinds of physical features are you most likely to find in Africa?

   A. frozen tundra, grasslands, rainforests, plateaus

   B. grasslands, mountains, rainforests, steppes

   C. rainforests, grasslands, deserts, plateaus

   D. mountains, tundra, steppes, rainforests

2. Which river is located in Southern Africa?

   A. Nile   C. Congo

   B. Niger   D. Zambezi

3. Although Ethiopia is close to the Equator, it tends to have mild temperatures because most of Ethiopia is

   A. at sea level.

   B. on a very high plateau.

   C. kept cool by Arctic winds.

   D. covered by rain forests.

4. One of the best ways to describe Africa's economy is

   A. a mix of subsistence farming, cash crops, mining, and logging.

   B. mostly manufacturing.

   C. mining and technology services.

   D. mostly mining and manufacturing.

5. What is one problem African farmers face when they give up subsistence farming to raise cash crops?

   A. Farmers plant fewer crops that can completely meet a family's needs, which sometimes results in food shortages.

   B. Africa's climate does not support most cash crops, which creates a fiercely competitive market for the few cash crops that do grow.

   C. Cash crops require more land and there isn't any room to expand in the already crowded farm regions.

   D. Cash crops are slowly helping to improve Africa's economy and so far have created no problems.

6. By developing the ability to domesticate plants and animals, early farmers could now have

   A. decorative house plants and pets.

   B. settlements, because they no longer had to travel to find food.

   C. nomadic lifestyles, because they knew where to go to find food.

   D. settlements, because they could trade domesticated plants and animals for food.

7. The ancient civilization in Egypt was ruled by pharaohs who were

   A. kings from Nubia and Ethiopia.

   B. kings who were also considered to be powerful priests.

   C. wealthy governors of large city-states.

   D. kings and queens who were also considered to be gods.

Name _____ Class _____ Date_____

Africa Benchmark Test 1 (continued)

Use the map <u>and</u> your knowledge of social studies to answer question 8.

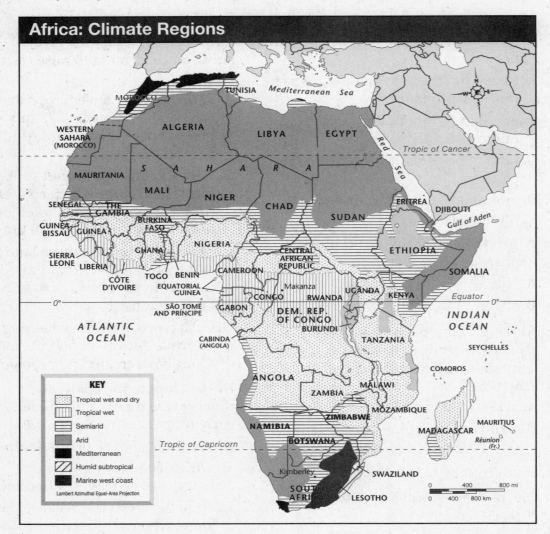

Africa: Climate Regions

KEY
- Tropical wet and dry
- Tropical wet
- Semiarid
- Arid
- Mediterranean
- Humid subtropical
- Marine west coast

Lambert Azimuthal Equal-Area Projection

8. In which two regions are most of Africa's rain forests located?

   A. North Africa and South Africa

   B. West Africa and East Africa

   C. East Africa and Southern Africa

   D. West Africa and Central Africa

9. Carthage, a wealthy Phoenician city-state, was

   A. captured by Rome and rebuilt to reflect Roman ideals.

   B. captured by the Arabs and rebuilt to reflect Arabic ideals.

   C. weakened and then eventually destroyed during wars with Rome.

   D. weakened and then eventually destroyed during wars with the Arabs.

Africa Proficiency Test 1 (continued)

10. How did African slave practices before the 1500s differ from European slave practices in the Americas?

    A. Europeans often freed their slaves after a few years.

    B. Europeans welcomed freed slaves into important roles in their community.

    C. Africans often treated their slaves like property and refused to free them.

    D. Africans often allowed slaves to be bought out of slavery by their own people.

11. Which of the following lists is in correct chronological order?

    A. Portuguese explored Africa's coast; Europeans settled in Africa; Atlantic Slave Trade began.

    B. Europeans settled in Africa; Portuguese explored Africa's coast; Atlantic Slave Trade began.

    C. Europe colonizes Africa; Atlantic Slave Trade begins; Portuguese explored Africa's coast.

    D. Portuguese explored Africa's coast; Atlantic Slave Trade begins; Europe colonizes Africa.

12. Nationalism among African countries in the 1900s led to

    A. peaceful transitions of power from European colonies to African governments.

    B. immediate democratic governments in most African countries.

    C. conflict, protest, and sometimes war followed by independence from European colonizers.

    D. strong leadership among new governments.

13. One environmental challenge facing Africa today is

    A. low literacy rates.

    B. soil erosion.

    C. overcrowded schools.

    D. specialized economies.

14. Muslim culture in North Africa has

    A. not been influenced by Western culture.

    B. had little cultural diffusion.

    C. been influenced by Berbers as well as Arabs and other ethnic groups.

    D. been abandoned in favor of traditional ways.

15. Societies in West Africa value

    A. very few other ethnic groups.

    B. kinship and extended family.

    C. urbanization.

    D. new traditions that move away from storytelling.

Africa Proficiency Test 1 (continued)

16. How has the United States been influenced by West Africa?

    A. Slaves brought their ideas, stories, dances, music, and customs with them.

    B. Many early American settlers studied the customs of West Africans.

    C. More American tourists visit West Africa today than any other foreign region.

    D. Slaves brought their books, their art, and many of their personal belongings with them.

17. Traditionally, Africans feel a strong bond to the land where they grow up. In fact, many East Africans consider

    A. living in the cities far superior to living in the rural areas.

    B. living in the cities better than living outside of Africa.

    C. living and working in the cities as a temporary duty.

    D. living and working in the rural areas as a temporary duty.

18. Why did apartheid finally end in South Africa?

    A. F.W. de Klerk decided to end apartheid because he felt it was wrong.

    B. Protests in South Africa and economic sanctions by foreign nations made the government realize that it was time to end apartheid.

    C. Mohandas Gandhi led a movement to end apartheid.

    D. Joseph Mobutu invaded South Africa, took over the government, and declared apartheid over.

19. Industry in South Africa created new roles for Africa's women by requiring

    A. women to start making household and community decisions while the men were away.

    B. women to join the work force in order to fill the growing number of job openings.

    C. men to stay at home and tend to house and family while women went to work.

    D. women to stay at home and tend to house and family while the men went to work.

20. Which of the following statements BEST describes South Africa?

    A. South Africa is diverse in both the people who live there and the rural and urban lifestyles in which the people live.

    B. Most people in South Africa are of European descent with very few blacks.

    C. All of the Africans who are of European descent in South Africa speak English.

    D. Although there are a few large villages and a couple small cities in South Africa, there are no large cities.

Name _____ Class _____ Date_____

Africa Benchmark Test 2

Directions: *Read each question and choose the best answer. Then mark the letter for the answer you have chosen.*

Use the diagram <u>and</u> your knowledge of social studies to answer questions 1-2.

Egypt United by Islam

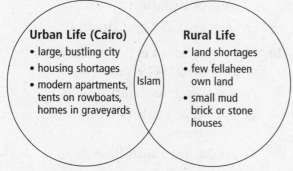

Islam helps Egyptians in both urban and rural areas to maintain traditional values and customs.

1. Based on the information in the diagram above, which of the following conclusions can be drawn?

   A. Because people live in tents and small stone houses, the country is not very advanced technologically.

   B. All people in Egypt are poor and cannot afford to own land or live in modern houses.

   C. Most Egyptians prefer rural life.

   D. The housing and land shortages indicate that parts of Egypt have high population densities.

2. Many Muslims believe that the laws of Egypt should be based on

   A. Islam.

   B. democratic ideals.

   C. protection of landowners.

   D. city experiences.

3. The Aswan High Dam helps deliver water to Egypt's cities and rural areas, but it's also causing

   A. the Nile Delta to shrink, because the dam blocks rich silt from being able to reach the delta.

   B. a cleaner and safer water supply, because it blocks silt from entering and polluting the water of the delta.

   C. better agricultural production, because it has opened new routes for rich silt to be delivered directly to farmland.

   D. more air pollution.

4. What is the name for open-air marketplaces in Algeria?

   A. fellaheens

   B. bazaars

   C. souqs

   D. casbahs

5. _____ is the official language of Nigeria, although most of the people of Nigeria speak _____.

   A. English, more than 200 other languages

   B. Nigerian, English

   C. English, Nigerian

   D. Nigerian, more than 200 other languages

Africa Benchmark Test 2 (continued)

6. From 1914 to 1960, the Nigerian government was under the control of
   A. Portugal.
   B. Great Britain.
   C. the Netherlands.
   D. the Yoruba.

7. The main ethnic groups in Nigeria are
   A. Igbo, English, and Berber.
   B. Yoruba, Igbo, and Hausa-Fulani.
   C. Spanish, Fulani, and Hausa.
   D. French, Abuja, and Igbo.

8. Nine years after being carried through the streets as a hero, Kwame Nkrumah of Ghana was thrown out of office because the people blamed him for the
   A. country's economic problems.
   B. growth of West African traditions.
   C. conflicts between ethnic groups.
   D. desertification of the Sahel.

9. Two causes of desertification in Mali are
   A. overpopulation and drought.
   B. overgrazing and torrential rains.
   C. industrialization and overpopulation.
   D. overgrazing and drought.

10. Mali's savanna is the one area of the country that receives
    A. economic assistance.
    B. very few visitors from other countries.
    C. abundant rainfall.
    D. no rainfall.

11. People in Ethiopia practice which of the following religions?
    A. Buddhism, Hinduism
    B. Islam, Christianity
    C: Judaism, Buddhism
    D. Islam, Hinduism

Africa Benchmark Test 2 *(continued)*

12. How did Julius Nyerere try to shape policy so that Tanzanians would feel more unified?

  A. He encouraged citizens to speak multiple languages rather than Swahili.

  B. He created multiple political parties based on ethnic groups so that each ethnic group had a voice in the government.

  C. He created a one-party system and gave voters a choice of candidates from that party.

  D. He encouraged borrowing from foreign nations.

13. What have Kenyan women accomplished with the self-help groups that have started in rural areas?

  A. Women have started to move to Nairobi and find jobs there.

  B. Women have built nursery schools and water pipes for the community and loaned money for small businesses.

  C. Women have started writing books.

  D. Women have rejected their traditional ways.

14. What is one example of how harambee affects life in Kenya?

  A. People place little value on their family relationships.

  B. People work together in villages to build schools.

  C. People leave Kenya to live in other countries.

  D. People refuse to help other villagers farm their land.

15. Belgium ruled the Congo in order to control the country's

  A. manufacturing.

  B. copper and diamonds.

  C. forestry and water.

  D. crops and wildlife.

16. What is the BEST way to describe the leadership of Joseph Mobuto of Zaire?

  A. He set up an authoritarian government, nationalized industries, and borrowed money from foreign governments.

  B. He set up a democratic government and privatized industry.

  C. He set up a socialist government and started sending money overseas.

  D. He set up a communist government, nationalized industries, and borrowed money from foreign governments.

Africa Benchmark Test 2 (continued)

17. After rebellions that began in 1996, Zaire had a new leader and was renamed the Democratic Republic of the Congo, but the country still faced civil war. How was Congo's civil war unique?

A. It was the first time a coup had been successfully committed in Africa.

B. It was the first time an African nation attempted to re-establish European rule.

C. It was the first war in post-independence Africa to involve several African nations.

D. It was the first attempt at democracy by any African nation.

18. By 1910, conflict over the control of land in South Africa erupted between which two groups?

A. French and Afrikaners

B. Dutch and Afrikaners

C. Arabs and Afrikaners

D. British and Afrikaners

19. What was the system of apartheid as practiced in South Africa?

A. An economic system that divides people and is primarily based on wealth.

B. A political system that divides people and is primarily based on political beliefs.

C. A legal system that discriminates against people and is primarily based on race.

D. A social system that discriminates against people and is primarily based on gender.

20. Who did South Africans elect as their new president after the end of apartheid?

A. Mobutu Sese Seko

B. Nelson Mandela

C. Kwame Nkrumah

D. F.W. de Klerk

Asia and the Pacific Benchmark Test 1

Directions: *Read each question and choose the best answer. Then mark the letter for the answer you have chosen.*

1. Which of the following describes a major physical feature of Japan?

   A. Japan is a desert.

   B. Japan is a peninsula.

   C. Japan is an archipelago.

   D. Japan is a large plateau.

2. How do farmers in East Asia produce enough food to feed the country's large population?

   A. They import rice and wheat from Europe.

   B. They use terrace farming and double-cropping methods.

   C. They dig deep irrigation channels to funnel water to mountain farmland.

   D. They grow rice in the mountains and wheat on the plateaus.

3. What powerful forces created the Himalayan Mountain range in Asia?

   A. Earthquakes spreading over the Indian subcontinent folded and buckled the land before splitting it into two regions.

   B. Widespread erosion cause by huge flooded rivers dramatically changed the shape of the land.

   C. The Indian subcontinent collided with Asia, and northern India and southern Asia crumpled where they met.

   D. Fast-flowing rivers carved deep canyons throughout the subcontinent of India, depositing heavy amounts of silt along their banks.

Use the graph and your knowledge of social studies to answer question 4.

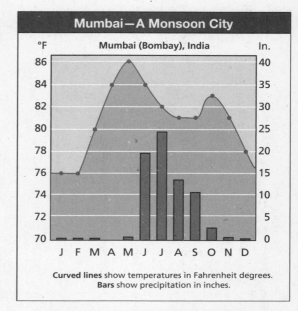

Mumbai—A Monsoon City

Mumbai (Bombay), India

Curved lines show temperatures in Fahrenheit degrees. **Bars** show precipitation in inches.

4. Look at the graph. What effect do the summer monsoons have on the temperature in Mumbai, India?

   A. The summer monsoons increase the usually cool temperatures of Mumbai.

   B. The summer monsoons maintain the average temperatures of Mumbai so that the crops can grow.

   C. The summer monsoons have nothing to do with the temperatures of Mumbai.

   D. The summer monsoons cool the very hot temperatures of Mumbai.

Asia and the Pacific Benchmark Test 1 (continued)

Use the map <u>and</u> your knowledge of social studies to answer questions 5–6.

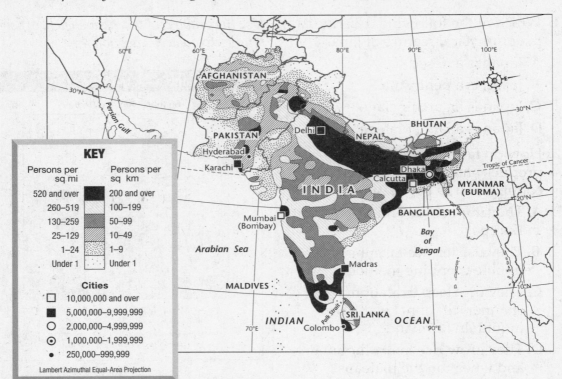

5. Which of the following countries has the most area with highest population density?

   A. Pakistan   C. Bangladesh

   B. Bhutan   D. Afghanistan

6. Based on the map, which of the following statements is correct?

   A. India is entirely south of the Tropic of Cancer.

   B. India is completely surrounded by the Arabian Sea.

   C. Sri Lanka is densely populated.

   D. Afghanistan is densely populated.

7. How does physical geography affect people in South and Southeast Asia?

   A. Physical geography affects life there only slightly. The rivers and the sea are used for transportation only.

   B. Mountainous regions make up 90 percent of the area, so travel is difficult but life is easy for the people who live there.

   C. Many people who live there live along the fertile river valleys and grow crops.

   D. Many people who live there grow such crops as corn and tobacco because of the dry conditions.

Asia and the Pacific Benchmark Test 1 *(continued)*

8. How have the climate conditions in Southwest and Central Asia affected farming?

   A. Because of the dry conditions, farmers must find ways to irrigate the farmland, such as with wadis, wells, and canals.

   B. No plants can grow in the region because it is too dry, so farmers have been forced to work in cities.

   C. Plants are easily sown in these areas, but because of the extremely cool temperatures, most planted crops die.

   D. The Mediterranean climate in Central Asia provides enough water for the limited farmland in Southwest Asia.

9. The nations of Singapore, Malaysia, Brunei, Indonesia, and the Philippines form

   A. island Southeast Asia.

   B. South Asia.

   C. the Indian subcontinent.

   D. mainland Southeast Asia.

10. Why are many of the plants and animals of New Zealand and Australia unique?

   A. The unusual climate has forced the plants and animals to adapt.

   B. The plants and animals on these islands are isolated from others on Earth.

   C. The seasons in this hemisphere are the opposite of those in the United States.

   D. The scientists of these islands have been cross-pollinating and breeding plants and animals for some time.

11. Why does the majority of Australia's population live on the eastern and southeastern coasts?

   A. The coasts have Australia's most fertile farmland and receive ample rain.

   B. Areas west of the Great Dividing Land have not been explored.

   C. The eastern and southeastern coasts are the only areas of Australia with ports.

   D. The rest of the country receives too much rain throughout the year.

12. How do the people of North Island in New Zealand turn water into an important source of energy?

   A. They use the force from the waves crashing on the coastlines as a source of power.

   B. They use the steam from geysers as a source of electricity.

   C. They use the change in ocean tides as an energy source.

   D. They build dams where rivers meet the ocean to create electricity.

13. Geographers divide the Pacific islands into high islands and low islands. What forms low islands?

   A. Low islands are formed by basins and ranges.

   B. Low islands are formed by desertification.

   C. Low islands are formed by coral reefs or atolls.

   D. Low islands are formed completely by erosion.

Asia and the Pacific Benchmark Test 1 (continued)

14. In the Pacific islands, why do more people live on high islands than on low islands?

    A. because of the low islands' mountains

    B. because of the low islands' small size

    C. because of the low islands' fertile soil

    D. because of the high islands' sandy soil

15. Because the Pacific islands have few natural resources, the economies of the islands have been improved by farmers who cultivate what kind of crops?

    A. Crops that do not need tending

    B. Crops that grow easily in a tropical climate

    C. Crops that need little water

    D. Crops that can be sold for money

16. The two major rivers of South Asia are

    A. the Tigris and the Euphrates.

    B. the Indus and the Deccan.

    C. the Ghats and the Bengal.

    D. the Indus and the Ganges.

17. The two most important natural resources in Southwest Asia are

    A. timber and coal.

    B. petroleum and water.

    C. gold and copper.

    D. fertile soil and iron.

18. East Asia's ocean and inland waters led to the development of

    A. East Asia as a sea power.

    B. vast oil fields.

    C. aquaculture.

    D. service industries.

19. Which statement below is an example of climate affecting diet?

    A. Deciduous trees change with the seasons.

    B. Wheat grows in cooler climates, therefore people in northern China eat more noodles than rice.

    C. Small flowering plants grow in the deserts of China after a rain.

    D. Farmers cut terraces in hillsides to grow more crops.

20. North Korea and South Korea do not share their natural resources. Why not?

    A. North Korea does not want to export any of its natural resources.

    B. South Korea does not need any of North Korea's natural resources.

    C. The hostile political situation between the two countries affects their economic relationship.

    D. Both countries have no need to share natural resources.

Asia and the Pacific Benchmark Test 2

Directions: *Read each question and choose the best answer. Then mark the letter for the answer you have chosen.*

1. Three important contributions made by ancient Chinese engineers were digging canals, building dams and bridges, and

   A. printing with movable type.

   B. setting up irrigation systems.

   C. building the Taj Mahal.

   D. building armored warships.

2. How did the communist government in China try to solve the country's population problem?

   A. People were encouraged to have only one child per family.

   B. China continued to expand its borders into what was once southern Russia.

   C. Couples paid higher taxes for having fewer children.

   D. Single people received generous government financial support.

3. What was one result of the Aryan migration into South Asia during ancient times?

   A. The Aryans introduced Islam and established the Mughal Empire.

   B. The Aryans introduced Indo-European languages, such as Hindi.

   C. The Aryans separated South Asia into colonies and city-states.

   D. The Aryans established the East India Company which eventually brought about British rule.

Use the chart __and__ your knowledge of social studies to answer questions 4–5.

Old Ways	New Ways
kimonos, samurai headbands	Western-style clothing
bow	shake hands
palaces	skyscrapers
arts and crafts	contemporary billboards
mats and low tables to eat	chairs and high tables for eating
herbal cures	modern hospitals
3-wheeled cabs	high-speed trains

4. In the nineteenth-century United States, technological development caused transitions from traditional to modern and rural to urban. Based on the chart, in what areas has East Asia echoed these changes?

   A. Clothing, architecture, medicine, and transportation

   B. Farming, clothing, medicine, and industrialization

   C. Economics, family, medicine, and furniture

   D. Government, economics, clothing, medicine

5. Which statement below is a valid conclusion based on the information in the chart?

   A. Many East Asians live in modern cities, but avoid modern technology.

   B. East Asians follow old ways at work, but new ways at home.

   C. New ways of life do not include modern architecture.

   D. New ways of life in East Asia resemble life in many Western cities.

Asia and the Pacific Benchmark Test 2 *(continued)*

6. What is one important achievement of ancient Mesopotamian civilization?

   A. settlements in the New World

   B. a written code of law

   C. trade with China

   D. the discovery of gold

7. Mesopotamia became a center of farming and trade because it

   A. controlled an important trade route between the Persian Gulf and the Red Sea.

   B. was protected from invasion by the Atlas Mountains.

   C. had large amounts of oil and natural gas.

   D. had fertile soil left by flooding along the Tigris and Euphrates rivers.

8. Why has Southwest Asia suffered violent disputes for so many years?

   A. Without modern technology, the various cultures of Southwest Asia have had many conflicts over food.

   B. One political group has ruled the area for centuries, but attempted revolutions happen every few years.

   C. The area has suffered disputes for control of its many forests.

   D. It has been a crossroads for many different religions and ethnic groups, which has led to conflict.

9. After the Spanish-American war, which country did the United States gain control over?

   A. Philippines

   B. Indo-China

   C. Burma

   D. Siam

10. Which was the only country in Southeast Asia that was not under colonial rule by 1914?

    A. Brunei

    B. Siam

    C. Philippines

    D. Cambodia

11. Which of the following was an effect of colonial rule in Southeast Asia?

    A. Southeast Asians were forced to speak English so that they could communicate with foreign traders.

    B. The economy grew stronger with the help of a transportation network built by colonial rulers.

    C. When colonies were forced to grow cash crops, there was not enough food for people to eat.

    D. A number of countries attempted to invade parts of Southeast Asia, so the production of staple products, such as rice, dramatically increased.

Asia and the Pacific Benchmark Test 2 *(continued)*

12. In what way is the history of New Zealand and Australia similar to that of the United States?

    A. They were all inhabited by Maoris.

    B. They were all colonized by Great Britain.

    C. They were all inhabited by Aborigines.

    D. They were all colonized by Spain.

13. Why did the British decide to settle the first colony in Australia?

    A. The British needed more land for New Zealand's exploding population.

    B. The British needed to develop a new trade route to Southeast Asia.

    C. The British wanted to spread Christianity to the Aborigines.

    D. The British wanted to start a penal colony there.

14. Like the Native American culture in America after the arrival of European settlers, the Maori culture

    A. was strengthened by contact with European settlers.

    B. was in danger of being destroyed before contact with European settlers.

    C. was in danger of being destroyed by contact with European settlers.

    D. was honored by English settlers.

15. Concern about the spread of communism involved the United States in a war in

    A. Taiwan.

    B. Vietnam.

    C. the Philippines.

    D. Thailand.

16. The leader of India's independence movement in the 1900s was

    A. Shah Jahan.

    B. Mumtaz Mahal.

    C. Mohandas K. Gandhi.

    D. Maurya Gupta.

17. Siddhartha Gautama's teachings influenced

    A. the development of culture in India, China, and Southeast Asia.

    B. architectural styles in the United States and Canada.

    C. the development of the novel.

    D. Chandragupta.

18. When Israel was declared a state in 1948

    A. many Jews resettled in Israel.

    B. hundreds of thousands of Palestinians fled Israeli territory.

    C. Arab nations invaded Israel.

    D. all of the above

Asia and the Pacific Benchmark Test 2 (continued)

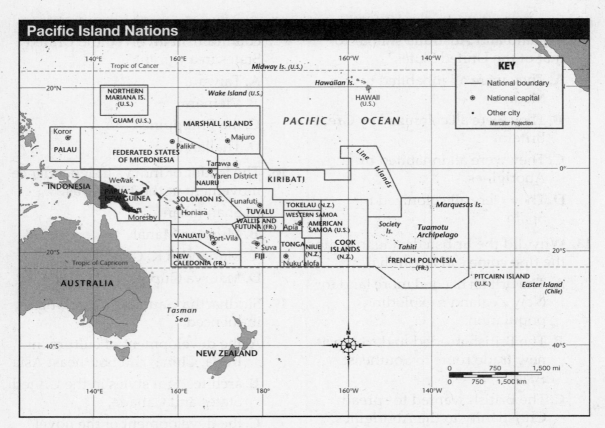

Pacific Island Nations

19. According to this map, which of the following is the BEST explanation as to why the people on each island in the Pacific developed their own language, customs, and religious beliefs?

   A. Distances between islands prevented communication between them.

   B. Each island was settled by a group from a different nation.

   C. The British wanted to keep each island colony independent.

   D. Bitter rivalries developed between islands over rights to waterways.

20. Which of the following is the BEST explanation for the many different religions followed by the people of Southeast Asia?

   A. Southeast Asian culture encourages young people to find their own religion.

   B. Colonial rulers demanded that people convert to Christianity.

   C. Actually, Hinduism is the primary religion in Southeast Asia.

   D. Through trade, conquest, and colonial rule, Southeast Asians have been introduced to many different religions.

Asia and the Pacific Proficiency Test 3

Directions: *Read each question and choose the best answer. Then mark the letter for the answer you have chosen.*

Use the chart __and__ your knowledge of social studies to answer questions 1-2.

China's Ecomony	
1950s:	Mao Zedong institutes new policies—Great Leap Forward and Cultural Revolution; Communist government owns all land, factories, and businesses.
1970s:	Moderate communism; free enterprise; people can choose jobs, start businesses, and make a profit.
1980s and 1990s:	Schools, parks, libraries, and skyscrapers built; streets are full of cars, trucks, and buses.
Today:	China is a world economic force.

1. In an attempt to increase output, China's Mao Zedong began which of the following policies?
   - A. Great Leap Forward
   - B. Communist Revolution
   - C. Revolution of Culture
   - D. Red Guard

2. Following Mao Zedong's death, what did moderate Communists in China do to improve the Chinese economy?
   - A. They introduced a radical policy called the Cultural Revolution.
   - B. They gradually introduced the Great Leap Forward.
   - C. They gradually allowed some free enterprise.
   - D. The government took control of all the land, factories, and businesses in China.

3. After World War II, the Japanese government helped build the economy by
   - A. providing farmland for all citizens.
   - B. allowing limited free enterprise.
   - C. giving subsidies to industries.
   - D. diversifying the economy.

4. The weaponless area that separates North and South Korea is called the
   - A. industrial zone.
   - B. central plateau.
   - C. border patrol.
   - D. demilitarized zone.

5. What keeps North and South Korea from forming one nation?
   - A. political differences
   - B. civil war
   - C. cultural differences
   - D. language differences

6. As a result of ongoing government efforts, India's life expectancy and literacy rates are
   - A. worsening slowly.
   - B. improving quickly.
   - C. staying about the same.
   - D. keeping pace with other countries.

Asia and the Pacific Benchmark Test 3 (continued)

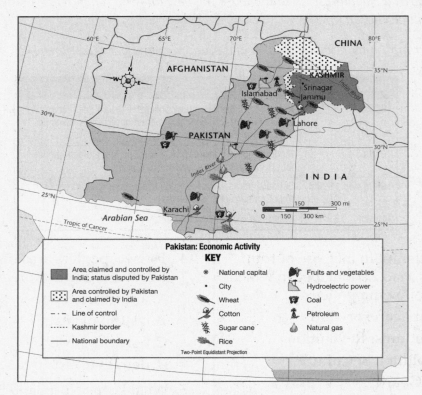

Use the map __and__ your knowledge of social studies to answer questions 7–8.

7. Which statement best describes the Indus River?

A. The Indus River flows through Kashmir and then enters India.

B. Too much rain in Pakistan causes the Indus River to flood, which makes farming difficult.

C. The Indus River flows through Kashmir and then into Pakistan.

D. The city of Islamabad is located near the mouth of the Indus River.

8. A main source of energy for industry in Pakistan is

A. hydroelectric dams.

B. wind power.

C. petroleum.

D. solar power.

9. The Saudi Arabian government is based on

A. unwritten traditions.

B. a written constitution.

C. the policies of a dictator.

D. the Quran and Islamic law.

10. Which of the following is a major environmental challenge for Kazakhstan?

A. Air pollution caused by fumes from car exhausts.

B. Radiation pollution caused by nuclear tests conducted by the Soviet Union.

C. Modern factories are dumping industrial waste into rivers and lakes.

D. Landfills are overflowing with solid waste, and there are no recycling programs.

Asia and the Pacific Benchmark Test 3 *(continued)*

Use the time line __and__ your knowledge of social studies to answer questions 11–12.

Time Line of Vietnamese History

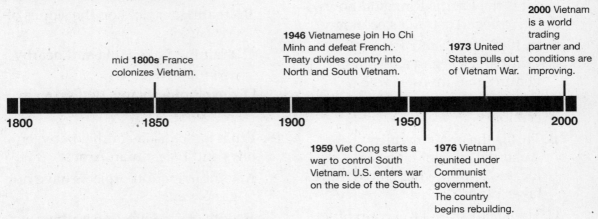

Vietnam is finally at peace and on the road to prosperity.

11. For how many years was the United States involved in the Vietnam War?

A. 14 years

B. 30 years

C. 59 years

D. 76 years

12. In the years since the Vietnam War, Vietnam's greatest successes have been in

A. developing agriculture

B. exporting electronic goods

C. rebuilding its cities

D. preserving its cultural heritage

13. On what are the economies of both Australia and New Zealand largely based?

A. service industries

B. tourism

C. agriculture and trade

D. manufacturing

14. Of what is Australia the world's largest exporter?

A. wheat

B. wool

C. sugar cane

D. bananas

Asia and the Pacific Benchmark Test 3 (continued)

15. As in the United States, economic activities around the world are affected by physical characteristics. What is the Pacific Rim, and how does it affect Australia's economy?

    A. In 1980, the Pacific Rim Companies began a business venture that invests large amounts of money in Australia's economy.

    B. This is the area in which Australia's major cities are located and in which most trade takes place.

    C. The Pacific Rim is a group of countries that signed a treaty promising they would provide economic and military support for Australia.

    D. These are the nations that border the Pacific Ocean and with which Australia has formed its closest economic ties.

16. Which statement about Japan's population density and geography is true?

    A. Japan's population is sparse and spread out over Japan's large, fertile plains.

    B. Japan's rugged geography has led to its large population to settle in concentrated cities.

    C. Japan's large population is spread out over its large, fertile plains.

    D. Japan's sparse population is mostly located in cities and suburbs.

17. Israel created additional farmland by

    A. purchasing land from Lebanon.

    B. creating terraces on the slopes of Mt. Sinai.

    C. draining Lake Hula and nearby swamps.

    D. developing plants that grow in saltwater.

18. What has caused conflict between Jews and Palestinian Arabs?

    A. Joint irrigation projects have not gone well.

    B. Both claim Palestine as their homeland.

    C. The disposal of nuclear waste has caused problems.

    D. One has a Communist government, while the other is an absolute monarchy.

19. In Saudi Arabia in the 1930s, poor towns became wealthy cities when

    A. Saudis funded education.

    B. a telephone system was installed to aid business.

    C. Saudi students learned to read and write.

    D. oil was discovered in Southwest Asia.

20. One problem facing the Stans is how to export their natural resources since the countries are

    A. polluted.

    B. surrounded by oceans.

    C. on the ancient Silk Road.

    D. landlocked.

The Ancient World Proficiency Test 1

Directions: *Read each question and choose the best answer. Then mark the letter for the answer you have chosen.*

1. What event ended prehistoric times and started history?
   A. Fire was invented.
   B. The wheel was invented.
   C. Writing was invented.
   D. People began to migrate to other regions.

2. What allowed humans to move to cold climates?
   A. They invented stone tools.
   B. They invented metal tools.
   C. They learned how to create fire.
   D. They learned how to make warm clothing.

3. How do archaeologists mark the start of the New Stone Age?
   A. People made stone tools and weapons.
   B. People learned how to plant crops.
   C. People stopped being nomads.
   D. People moved to colder climates.

4. During the New Stone Age, food surpluses allowed more people to become
   A. farmers.
   B. fishers.
   C. gatherers.
   D. artisans.

5. Some of the earliest cities started in the Fertile Crescent because
   A. important metals were found there.
   B. the Nile River allowed easy transportation.
   C. the area was easy to defend.
   D. the rivers there created rich farmland.

6. Why do we know so much about the Assyrian Empire?
   A. The Assyrians built a great library.
   B. The Assyrians invented the battering ram.
   C. The Assyrians had many friends.
   D. The Assyrian armies won many battles.

7. Hammurabi's Code was important because
   A. it was based on oral traditions.
   B. Babylonia ruled the ancient world.
   C. the laws treated everyone the same.
   D. for the first time, laws were written down.

The Ancient World Benchmark Test 1 (continued)

8. The Phoenician alphabet made it easier for people to
   A. hire scribes.
   B. learn cuneiform.
   C. teach cuneiform.
   D. learn to read and write.

9. Who first taught the Israelites to practice monotheism?
   A. Abraham
   B. Hammurabi
   C. Saul
   D. David

10. Judaism had a great influence on
    A. Christianity.
    B. Islam.
    C. both Christianity and Islam.
    D. neither Christianity nor Islam.

11. The leader of ancient Egypt is known as
    A. a pharaoh.
    B. a dynasty.
    C. a kingdom.
    D. Amon-Re.

12. Many Nubians were in the Egyptian army because they were
    A. slaves.
    B. allies.
    C. conquered.
    D. expert archers.

13. The great barrier north of India is the
    A. Indian Ocean.
    B. Himalayas.
    C. Ganges River.
    D. Indus River.

The Ancient World Proficiency Test 1 (continued)

14. India's society is divided into groups that Europeans called
A. occupations.
B. clans.
C. priests.
D. castes.

15. Reincarnation is a Hindu belief
A. that describes the beginning of the world.
B. that explains why people suffer.
C. where, after death, the soul is reborn in another living thing.
D. where there are many gods.

Use the information found in Hammurabi's Code and your knowledge of social studies to answer questions 16-17.

Hammurabi's Code

- If any one steal the minor son of another, he shall be put to death.
- If any one is committing a robbery and is caught, then he shall be put to death.
- If any one open his ditches to water his crop, but is careless, and the water flood the field of his neighbor, then he shall pay his neighbor corn for the loss.
- If a man adopt a child [as his] son, and rear him, this grown son cannot be demanded back again.
- If a son strike his father, his hands shall be hewn (cut) off.

---

16. The laws in the code above cover the following categories:
A. labor, property, military
B. family, robbery, property
C. medicine, military, property
D. family, transportation, labor

17. According to Hammurabi's Code, death was the penalty for
A. a son striking his father.
B. a man adopting and rearing another man's child.
C. a man accidentally flooding his neighbor's field.
D. robbery or kidnapping.

The Ancient World Benchmark Test 1 (continued)

Use the timeline __and__ your knowledge of social studies to answer questions 18-19.

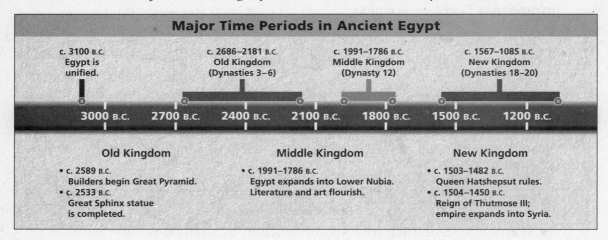

Major Time Periods in Ancient Egypt

c. 3100 B.C.
Egypt is
unified.

c. 2686–2181 B.C.
Old Kingdom
(Dynasties 3–6)

c. 1991–1786 B.C.
Middle Kingdom
(Dynasty 12)

c. 1567–1085 B.C.
New Kingdom
(Dynasties 18–20)

3000 B.C.   **2700** B.C.   **2400** B.C.   **2100** B.C.   **1800** B.C.   **1500** B.C.   **1200** B.C.

Old Kingdom
- c. 2589 B.C.
  Builders begin Great Pyramid.
- c. 2533 B.C.
  Great Sphinx statue
  is completed.

Middle Kingdom
- c. 1991–1786 B.C.
  Egypt expands into Lower Nubia.
  Literature and art flourish.

New Kingdom
- c. 1503–1482 B.C.
  Queen Hatshepsut rules.
- c. 1504–1450 B.C.
  Reign of Thutmose III;
  empire expands into Syria.

18. Egypt's history is divided into major time periods called
   A. dynasties.
   B. pharaohs.
   C. kingdoms.
   D. provinces.

19. During which two time periods was Egypt most stable?
   A. Old Kingdom and Middle Kingdom
   B. Middle Kingdom and New Kingdom
   C. Old Kingdom and New Kingdom
   D. Egypt did not experience stability.

20. Which of the following is a true statement about the Maurya Empire?
   A. During Chandragupta's rule, the Maurya Empire declined.
   B. Asoka required that Indians convert to Islam.
   C. The Maurya Empire closed its borders to foreign trade.
   D. The Maurya Empire was a great empire of India.

The Ancient World Benchmark Test 2

Directions: *Read each question and choose the best answer. Then mark the letter for the answer you have chosen.*

1. How are China's rivers like Egypt's Nile River?
   A. In both countries, the rivers flow north.
   B. In both countries, the rivers flood every spring.
   C. In both countries, the rivers dry up in the summer.
   D. In both countries, the rivers resemble dragons.

2. In ancient China, the most important segment of society was
   A. the nation.
   B. the individual.
   C. the village.
   D. the family.

3. How did the ideas of Confucius influence government?
   A. Government posts were given to the sons of the wealthy.
   B. Warriors fought each other for government jobs.
   C. Government jobs were given to people based on merit.
   D. Priests became major government officials.

4. Shi Huangdi made
   A. the first currency in China.
   B. the decision that all of China should use the same currency.
   C. all of China's people pay taxes.
   D. no changes to China's currency.

5. The main interest of the Chinese emperor Wudi was
   A. encouraging all Chinese people to read and write.
   B. improving Chinese society.
   C. conquering other lands.
   D. building the power of the warlords.

6. The Silk Road was built
   A. to help Chinese armies travel faster.
   B. to spread Confucianism.
   C. to import silk into China.
   D. to enable trade with the West.

The Ancient World Benchmark Test 2 (continued)

7. An important Chinese accomplishment during the Han Dynasty was
   A. the invention of paper.
   B. the construction of the Great Wall.
   C. the construction of the Silk Road.
   D. the creation of a new alphabet.

8. Greece's geographical features include
   A. large plains.
   B. the Himalayas.
   C. deserts.
   D. mountains and rocky islands.

9. Two early Greek cultures were
   A. Minoan and Mycenaen.
   B. Minoan and Egyptian.
   C. Mycenaen and Turkish.
   D. Minoan and Turkish.

10. After the Trojan War ended
    A. many Greeks built Trojan horses.
    B. Greece fell into the Dark Ages.
    C. Greek civilization prospered.
    D. Troy became a great city.

11. The rise of the merchant class in Greece led to
    A. great armies of chariots.
    B. democracy.
    C. very little change in government.
    D. richer aristocrats.

12. Socrates, Plato, and Aristotle were
    A. philosophers.
    B. soldiers.
    C. oracles.
    D. gods.

13. Ancient Sparta spent most of its resources on
    A. works of art.
    B. merchants.
    C. recreation.
    D. the military.

The Ancient World Benchmark Test 2 (continued)

Use the map and your knowledge of social studies to answer question 14.

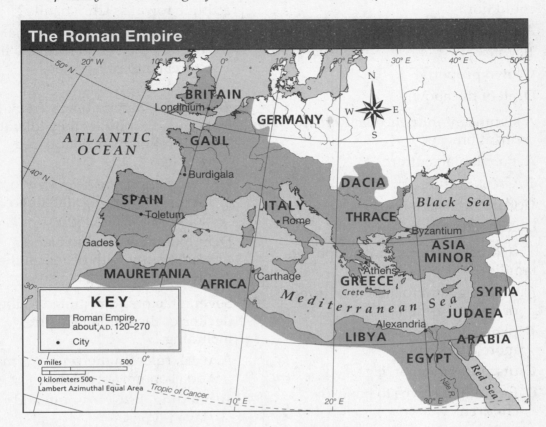

The Roman Empire

KEY
Roman Empire, about A.D. 120–270
• City

0 miles 500
0 kilometers 500
Lambert Azimuthal Equal Area

14. According to the map, the Roman Empire surrounded

  A. Eastern and Western Europe.

  B. only Italy.

  C. only Germany.

  D. the entire Mediterranean Sea.

15. After conquering the last Etruscan king, the Romans were governed by

  A. a republic in which citizens voted for their leaders.

  B. their own king.

  C. a council of religious leaders.

  D. one tyrant after another.

The Ancient World Benchmark Test 2 (continued)

16. Athenian women in Ancient Greece could not
    A. take part in politics.
    B. vote.
    C. own property.
    D. all of the above

17. A significant influence on Roman civilization was
    A. Babylonian culture.
    B. Greek culture.
    C. Carthaginian culture.
    D. Minoan culture.

18. The Roman government supported families by
    A. granting land to fathers of three or more children.
    B. penalizing families with two or more children.
    C. discouraging marriage.
    D. forbidding slaves to have children.

19. What was the Roman Empire's attitude towards Christianity?
    A. At first, it was Rome's official religion, then emperors saw it as a threat and persecuted members.
    B. The religion was tolerated by the Roman Empire, as they tolerated most religions of conquered peoples.
    C. The religion was seen as a threat for many years, but later became Rome's official religion.
    D. Emperors wanted to blend Christianity with beliefs in their own gods.

20. Several factors contributed to the decline of the Roman Empire, including
    A. weak rulers, a mercenary army, and economic problems.
    B. building the Colosseum and slave revolts.
    C. the size of the empire, the five good emperors, and the Pax Romana.
    D. weak rulers, aqueducts, and Christianity.

Medieval Times to Today Benchmark Test 1

Directions: *Read each question and choose the best answer. Then mark the letter for the answer you have chosen.*

Use the map and your knowledge of social studies to answer question 1.

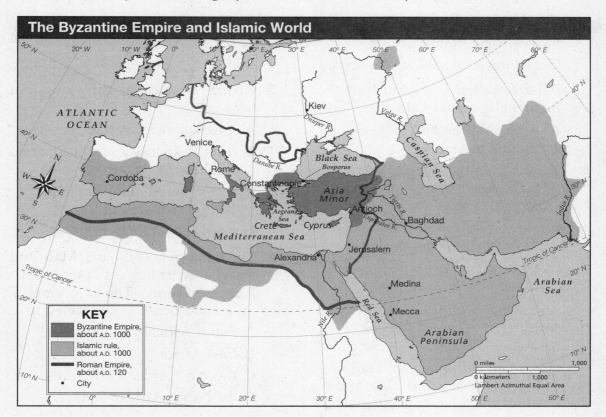

The Byzantine Empire and Islamic World

1. Which of the following statements is based on information from the map?

   A. The Byzantine Empire was the largest of the three empires.

   B. The Roman Empire followed Islamic rule.

   C. The Byzantine Empire existed at the same time as Islamic rule.

   D. The Byzantine Empire influenced the development of the Roman Empire.

2. Justinian's Code was

   A. the basis for Morse Code.

   B. a code of behavior and courtesy.

   C. the basis for the legal systems of many modern countries.

   D. lost when the Turks captured Constantinople.

Medieval Times to Today Benchmark Test 1 *(continued)*

3. Which of the following is one of the Five Pillars of Islam?
   A. reading the Torah
   B. celebrating Easter
   C. wearing certain clothing
   D. making a pilgrimage to Mecca

4. After Arab scholars contributed to the development of algebra,
   A. Arab children had to pass algebra tests.
   B. later scientists used algebra to make discoveries in astronomy, physics, and chemistry.
   C. they organized the knowledge in a book called *Canon of Algebra*.
   D. Rumi used algebraic formulas to create whirling dervishes.

5. Scientists have found it difficult to study early African cultures because
   A. African cultures often made things out of wood, clay, and iron, which have disintegrated.
   B. scientists do not know the language.
   C. so few people lived in Africa that scientists have been unable to locate any settlements.
   D. each time the Bantu migrated, they destroyed their personal possessions.

6. One of the most important products traded in West Africa was
   A. copper.
   B. silver.
   C. salt.
   D. iron.

7. Ghana became a wealthy kingdom because
   A. it took control of trade routes.
   B. it sold expensive slaves to Great Zimbabwe.
   C. it conquered many enemies, taking their wealth.
   D. it was always at war.

8. The kingdoms of Ghana, Mali, and Songhai were located in the West African savanna. The kingdoms of Ile-Ife and Benin were located in
   A. South Africa.
   B. East Africa.
   C. the West African rain forest.
   D. the North African Sahara.

9. Within 150 years of Muhammad's death, Islam attracted many new converts including
   A. Christians along the Mediterranean.
   B. Christians in England.
   C. Buddhists in Japan.
   D. Native Americans.

Medieval Times to Today Benchmark Test 1 (continued)

Use the map and your knowledge of social studies to answer questions 10 and 11.

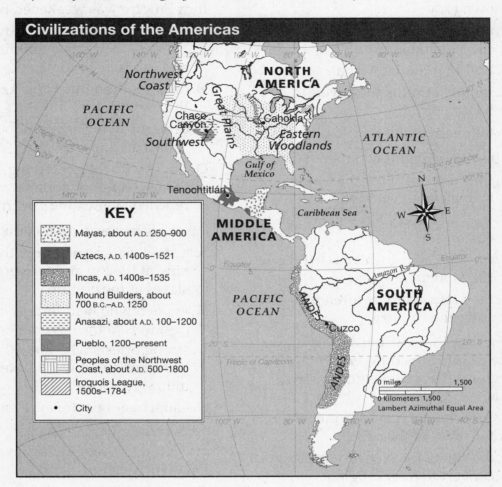

10. According to the map the earliest civilization in the Americas was the _____, located in _____.

   A. Incas, South America

   B. Mayas, Middle America

   C. Mound Builders, North America

   D. Pueblo, North America

11. The Incas developed terrace farming because they were

   A. on the Amazon River.

   B. in the Great Plains.

   C. on the rocky Northern Coast.

   D. in the Andes.

12. Slash-and-burn agriculture was

   A. a Mayan farming technique.

   B. an Aztec sacrifice for good crops.

   C. what Incas did to the land of people they conquered.

   D. an Iroquois farming technique.

13. The Grand Canal joined northern and southern China and

   A. protected the border from invaders.

   B. made it possible to bring grain into the capital.

   C. Tang Taizong decorated it with calligraphy.

   D. it crossed the Plateau of Tibet.

Medieval Times to Today Benchmark Test 1 (continued)

14. Akbar's grandson, Shah Jahan, is known for
   A. strengthening the government of the Mughal Empire.
   B. building the Taj Mahal.
   C. forcing Hindus to convert to Islam.
   D. taking over the Delhi Sultanate.

15. After the Mongols conquered China
   A. they did not allow the Chinese ruling class to govern.
   B. they adopted Chinese ways and customs.
   C. they forced the Chinese to follow the Mongol religion.
   D. they refused to let foreigners enter the country.

16. One way that Muslim culture under the caliphs was different from under the Byzantine Empire was that
   A. the scholars had little interest in the ideas of the past.
   B. the rulers forced everyone to convert to their religion.
   C. the rulers tolerated all faiths and allowed people to worship as they chose.
   D. their armies didn't try to conquer new lands.

17. Kilwa in East Africa was like Ghana and other West African civilizations in that
   A. most of its people were Bantu.
   B. its wealth came from taxes on trading goods.
   C. their most important trading products were salt and gold.
   D. they converted to Christianity in the 300s.

18. Before the Spanish attacked, the Inca Empire was weakened by
   A. earthquakes which destroyed many of their stone buildings and roads.
   B. diseases brought by the Aztecs to the north.
   C. droughts which caused food shortages and starvation.
   D. rulers who fought among themselves and workers who rebelled against the government.

19. Aztec society was characterized by
   A. a strict class structure with the king at the top and farmers and slaves at the bottom.
   B. women who held important positions in the government.
   C. strong priests who made decisions about work, taxes, and military attacks.
   D. equal treatment for everyone and laws against slavery.

20. The feudal system in medieval Japan included
   A. a strong emperor who was able to control landowners and use their wealth for trade.
   B. nobles who made treaties with kingdoms in China and Korea.
   C. landowners with large estates and their own armies of samurais.
   D. serfs who could be sold to other landowners.

Medieval Times to Today Benchmark Test 2

Directions: *Read each question and choose the best answer. Then mark the letter for the answer you have chosen.*

Use the map __and__ your knowledge of social studies to answer question 1.

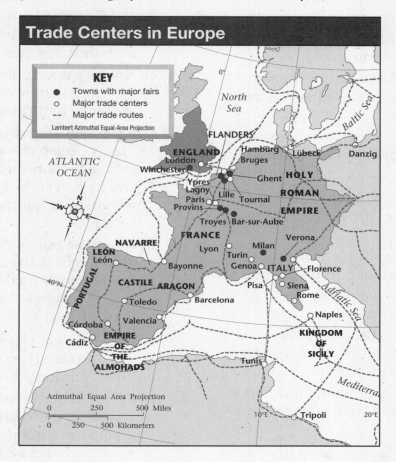

Trade Centers in Europe

KEY
- ● Towns with major fairs
- ○ Major trade centers
- -- Major trade routes

Lambert Azimuthal Equal-Area Projection

1. According to the map above, where did MOST European towns develop during the Middle Ages?

   A. They developed only on the coasts.

   B. They developed along trade routes and waterways.

   C. They developed in warmer climate areas.

   D. They developed where the land was most fertile.

Medieval Times to Today Benchmark Test 2 *(continued)*

2. The Middle Ages in Europe began

  A. about 800 when the Vikings attacked areas along the northern coast of Europe.

  B. about 1000 when the printing press was invented.

  C. about 500 when the Roman Empire collapsed in Western Europe.

  D. about 1095 when the first Crusades reached the Holy Land.

3. By the 1300s, towns and cities in Europe had grown very crowded, which led to

  A. the bubonic plague wiping out one third of Europe's population.

  B. architects building the first apartment houses.

  C. peasants becoming very powerful by forming groups to protect their rights.

  D. countries looking for colonies with land where people could move.

4. What was one cause of the Crusades?

  A. The Turks took over the Holy Land and would not let Christian pilgrims visit it.

  B. Arab people asked Christians to send missionaries.

  C. France wanted to open trade routes to the Americas.

  D. The Turks wanted to recapture Constantinople and much of the former Byzantine Empire.

5. How did the decline of feudalism affect the control of power in Europe?

  A. Nobles gained power because of new wealth they brought home from the Crusades.

  B. Nobles gained power because they collected money in exchange for protecting cities.

  C. Kings gained power because they collected money in exchange for protecting cities and took over the land of nobles who did not return from the Crusades.

  D. Kings lost power because they didn't fight in the Crusades, and the people refused to follow a king who was not willing to die for the Church.

6. Why did the Renaissance flower first in northern Italy rather than in northern Europe?

  A. People in northern Europe were accustomed to a great deal of leisure time, but people in northern Italy had to constantly work at survival.

  B. People in northern Europe lived under feudalism, but people in northern Italy lived in city-states that were more independent and less under the Church's control.

  C. People in northern Europe traded goods with India, but people in northern Italy traded goods only among themselves.

  D. People in northern Europe valued history and were skeptical of change, but people in northern Italy were accustomed to changes and innovations.

Medieval Times to Today Benchmark Test 2 (continued)

Use the outline __and__ your knowledge of social studies to answer question 7.

European Ages, 1200s to 1700s

I. Age of Discovery
   A. Exploration
      1. Marco Polo
   B. Renaissance
      1. learning
      2. literature, art, architecture
      3. humanism

II. Age of Revolution
   A. Government
      1. kings as absolute monarchs
      2. English king overthrown
      3. modern democracy begins
   B. Science
      1. Scientific Revolution
         a. scientific method
         b. astronomy, mathematics

---

7. The ideas of the Age of Revolution led to which of the following in European Countries?

A. monarchy and mob rule

B. the scientific revolution and the technological revolution

C. the modern age of science and democracy

D. exploration and humanism

8. Which of the following statements about Louis XIV of France is true?

A. He shared power with the nobles in the National Assembly.

B. He made alliances with other countries for their protection.

C. He opposed Cardinal Richelieu when he tried to reduce the power of the nobles.

D. He taxed the peasants heavily to support his luxurious lifestyle and many wars.

9. Which of the following is a factor that helped Elizabeth I of England establish her power in the 1500s?

A. Her father had broken from the Roman Catholic Church and started a Protestant church.

B. Her grandfather had already defeated France in a war.

C. She had signed the Magna Carta which gave her power over Parliament.

D. She refused to travel in England and required all nobles to come to the Tower of London.

10. How did Spanish citizens in the colony of New Spain treat Native Americans?

A. They set up schools for Native Americans to learn how to read.

B. They did not allow Native Americans to hold office unless they were elected by a majority.

C. They took control of the land and forced native people to work for no pay.

D. They kept things the same and only required native people to pay taxes.

11. The slave trade in Africa became a big business in the 1500s and grew larger when

A. colonies in the Americas began supplying slaves to Europe.

B. England began using slaves in the 1600s.

C. new trade routes were discovered to Asia.

D. colonies in the Americas needed workers.

Medieval Times to Today Benchmark Test 2 *(continued)*

12. John Locke was opposed to the monarchs of Europe during the Enlightenment because he believed

    A. scientists should run the government.

    B. the church should hold most of the power.

    C. kings or queens did not have divine rights.

    D. the Industrial Revolution was wrong.

13. Charles I was overthrown and executed, but later his son, Charles II, restored the monarchy in England when

    A. he agreed to an absolute monarchy.

    B. he and Parliament agreed to a limited monarchy.

    C. he publicly apologized for the errors of his father.

    D. he recaptured London and executed leaders.

14. The Reign of Terror occurred in which of the following countries?

    A. England   C. Russia

    B. Italy   D. France

15. Which of the following BEST describes the change that took place during the Industrial Revolution?

    A. The production of goods shifted from simple hand tools to complex machines.

    B. The government took over many farms to increase production.

    C. Conditions for workers improved greatly as a result of improvements in machinery.

    D. The quality of products increased because products were made by individual people.

16. When European nations divided up control of Africa in the 1880s, they were most interested in

    A. spreading Christianity.

    B. establishing new factories.

    C. controlling trade routes.

    D. the natural resources there.

17. How did the Great Depression affect the United States?

    A. It didn't affect the United States.

    B. It hurt relations between the United States and Canada.

    C. Many people left the United States for Europe.

    D. At one point, about one third of Americans could not find jobs.

18. During the Cold War, the United States and the Soviet Union supported hot wars in

    A. Korea and Vietnam.

    B. Korea and China.

    C. Germany and Poland.

    D. Japan and the Philippines.

19. After the Soviet Union collapsed in 1991, Russia established

    A. an agreement to join with China to form a new country.

    B. a new capital to increase its control in Eastern Europe.

    C. a new economy by changing to a capitalist system.

    D. new policies that broke off its relations with the United States.

20. Today, poverty is a problem

    A. only in Asia.

    B. in Asia, Africa, and Latin America.

    C. solved by trading blocs.

    D. that doesn't affect health care or nutrition in most of the world.

Foundations of Geography Benchmark
Answer Key

Test 1

1. D	11. B
2. D	12. A
3. C	13. A
4. B	14. B
5. C	15. D
6. C	16. B
7. B	17. B
8. A	18. D
9. A	19. C
10. D	20. D

Test 2

1. B	11. C
2. C	12. A
3. C	13. B
4. A	14. D
5. B	15. D
6. C	16. A
7. D	17. B
8. C	18. C
9. A	19. B
10. C	20. A

United States and Canada Benchmark
Answer Key

Test 1

1. C	11. C
2. D	12. A
3. B	13. A
4. A	14. D
5. C	15. C
6. C	16. B
7. B	17. D
8. A	18. C
9. D	19. A
10. B	20. A

Test 2

1. C	11. D
2. B	12. C
3. A	13. A
4. D	14. B
5. D	15. A
6. B	16. C
7. C	17. B
8. D	18. A
9. B	19. A
10. D	20. B

Latin America Benchmark Answer Key

Test 1   ## Test 2

1. B	11. A	1. B	11. A
2. D	12. A	2. D	12. B
3. C	13. C	3. C	13. D
4. A	14. A	4. D	14. C
5. C	15. B	5. A	15. A
6. D	16. C	6. B	16. A
7. D	17. A	7. A	17. B
8. C	18. A	8. A	18. D
9. B	19. C	9. C	19. D
10. A	20. D	10. B	20. C

Europe and Russia Benchmark Answer Key

Test 1   ## Test 2

1. C	11. C	1. A	11. D
2. B	12. C	2. C	12. A
3. A	13. A	3. C	13. A
4. D	14. B	4. D	14. C
5. B	15. C	5. B	15. C
6. A	16. A	6. A	16. B
7. C	17. B	7. D	17. A
8. C	18. D	8. B	18. D
9. D	19. D	9. C	19. C
10. A	20. B	10. B	20. B

Africa Benchmark Answer Key

Test 1

1. C	11. A
2. D	12. C
3. B	13. B
4. A	14. C
5. A	15. B
6. B	16. A
7. D	17. C
8. D	18. B
9. C	19. A
10. D	20. A

Test 2

1. D	11. B
2. A	12. C
3. A	13. B
4. C	14. B
5. A	15. B
6. B	16. A
7. B	17. C
8. A	18. D
9. D	19. C
10. C	20. B

Asia and the Pacific Benchmark Answer Key

Test 1

1. C	11. A
2. B	12. B
3. C	13. C
4. A	14. B
5. C	15. D
6. C	16. D
7. C	17. B
8. A	18. C
9. A	19. B
10. B	20. C

Test 2

1. B	11. B
2. A	12. B
3. B	13. D
4. A	14. C
5. D	15. B
6. B	16. C
7. D	17. A
8. D	18. D
9. A	19. A
10. B	20. D

Test 3

1. A	11. A
2. C	12. C
3. C	13. C
4. D	14. B
5. A	15. D
6. B	16. B
7. C	17. C
8. A	18. B
9. D	19. D
10. B	20. D

The Ancient World Benchmark Answer Key

Test 1

1. C	11. A
2. C	12. D
3. B	13. B
4. D	14. D
5. D	15. C
6. A	16. B
7. D	17. D
8. D	18. C
9. A	19. C
10. C	20. D

Test 2

1. B	11. B
2. D	12. A
3. C	13. D
4. B	14. D
5. C	15. A
6. D	16. D
7. A	17. B
8. D	18. A
9. A	19. C
10. B	20. A

Medieval Times to Today Benchmark Answer Key

Test 1

1. C	11. D
2. C	12. A
3. D	13. B
4. B	14. B
5. A	15. A
6. C	16. C
7. A	17. B
8. C	18. D
9. A	19. A
10. C	20. C

Test 2

1. B	11. D
2. C	12. C
3. A	13. B
4. A	14. D
5. C	15. A
6. B	16. D
7. C	17. D
8. D	18. A
9. A	19. C
10. C	20. B

Name_____ Class_____ Date_____

Report Sheet

Foundations of Geography Benchmark Test 1

Overall Score _____

Question	Chapter/Section		Standard	Needs Review	Reading and Vocabulary Study Guide pages		Completed
	Foundations of Geography	Eastern and Western Hemisphere			Foundations of Geography	Eastern and Western Hemisphere	
1.	1.1	1.1	NG 3		6-8	2-4	
2.	1.1	1.1	NG 1		6-8	2-4	
3.	1.1	1.1	NG 1		6-8	2-4	
4.	1.1	1.1	NG 5		6-8	2-4	
5.	1.1	1.1	NG 3		6-8	2-4	
6.	1.2	1.2	NG 1		9-11	5-7	
7.	1.2	1.2	NG 1		9-11	5-7	
8.	1.2	1.2	NG 1		9-11	5-7	
9.	1.2	1.2	NG 1		9-11	5-7	
10.	1.2	1.2	NG 1		9-11	5-7	
11.	2.1	2.1	NG 7		13-15	9-11	
12.	2.1	2.1	NG 7		13-15	9-11	
13.	2.1	2.1	NG 7		13-15	9-11	
14.	2.2	2.2	NG 7		16-18	12-14	
15.	2.2	2.2	NG 7		16-18	12-14	
16.	2.2	2.2	NG 4		16-18	12-14	
17.	2.3	2.3	NG 15		19-21	15-17	
18.	2.3	2.3	NG 7		19-21	15-17	
19.	2.4	2.4	NG 7		22-24	18-20	
20.	2.4	2.4	NG 7		22-24	18-20	

Name _____ Class _____ Date_____

Report Sheet

Foundations of Geography Benchmark Test 2

Overall Score _____

Question	Chapter/Section		Standard	Needs Review	Reading and Vocabulary Study Guide pages		Completed
	Foundations of Geography	Eastern and Western Hemisphere			Foundations of Geography	Eastern and Western Hemisphere	
1.	3.1	3.1	NG 9		26-28	22-24	
2.	3.1	3.1	NG 9		26-28	22-24	
3.	3.1	3.1	NG 9		26-28	22-24	
4.	3.2	3.2	NG 12		29-31	25-27	
5.	3.2	3.2	NG 12		29-31	25-27	
6.	3.2	3.2	NG 9		29-31	25-27	
7.	3.2	3.2	NG 9		32-34	25-27	
8.	3.3	3.3	NG 11		32-34	28-30	
9.	3.3	3.3	NG 11		32-34	28-30	
10.	3.4	3.4	NG 13		35-37	31-33	
11.	3.4	3.4	NG 13		35-37	31-33	
12.	4.1	4.1	NG 12		36-38	35-37	
13.	4.2	4.2	NG 6		39-41	38-40	
14.	4.3	4.3	NG 6		42-44	41-43	
15.	5.1	5.1	NG 8		49-51	45-47	
16.	5.1	5.1	NG 8		49-51	45-47	
17.	5.2	5.2	NG 8		52-54	48-50	
18.	5.2	5.2	NG 11		52-54	48-50	
19.	5.3	5.3	NG 14		55-57	51-53	
20.	5.3	5.3	NG 14		55-57	51-53	

Name _____ Class _____ Date_____

Report Sheet

United States and Canada Benchmark Test 1

Overall Score _____

Question	Chapter/Section		Standard	Needs Review	Reading and Vocabulary Study Guide pages		Completed
	United States and Canada	Western Hemisphere			United States and Canada	Western Hemisphere	
1.	1.1	6.1	NG 2, 4		6-8	56-58	
2.	1.1	6.1	NG 18		6-8	56-58	
3.	1.2	6.2	NG 15		9-11	59-61	
4.	1.3	6.3	NG 4		9-11	59-61	
5.	1.3	6.3	NG 11, 16		12-14	62-64	
6.	2.1	7.1	NG 13		16-18	66-68	
7.	2.1	7.1	NG 9, 13		16-18	66-68	
8.	2.2	7.2	NG 12		19-21	69-71	
9.	2.2	7.2	NG 13		19-21	69-71	
10.	2.3	7.3	NG 11		22-24	72-74	
11.	2.3	7.3	NG 13		22-24	72-74	
12.	2.2	7.2	NG 11		19-21	69-71	
13.	2.3	7.3	NG 13		22-24	72-74	
14.	2.5	7.5	NG 14		25-27	75-77	
15.	2.4	7.4	NG 9, 13		24-26	74-76	
16.	2.5	7.5	NG 14		28-30	78-80	
17.	3.1	8.1	NG 4, 10, 11		32-34	82-84	
18.	3.2	8.2	NG 10		35-37	85-87	
19.	3.3	8.3	NG 10		38-40	88-90	
20.	3.3	8.3	NG 4, 10, 15		38-40	88-90	

Report Sheet

United States and Canada Benchmark Test 2

Overall Score _____

Question	Chapter/Section		Standard	Needs Review	Reading and Vocabulary Study Guide pages		Completed
	United States and Canada	Western Hemisphere			United States and Canada	Western Hemisphere	
1.	4.1	9.1	NG 9, 10		42-44	92-94	
2.	4.2	9.2	NG 11		45-47	95-97	
3.	4.1	9.1	NG 2, 9		42-44	92-94	
4.	4.2	9.2	NG 9		45-47	95-97	
5.	4.3	9.3	NG 11		48-50	98-100	
6.	4.3	9.3	NG 11		48-50	98-100	
7.	4.4	9.4	NG 10, 12		51-53	101-103	
8.	4.4	9.4	NG 9, 12		51-53	101-103	
9.	5.1	10.1	NG 4		55-57	105-107	
10.	4.4	9.4	NG 11		51-53	101-103	
11.	5.1	10.1	NG 10		55-57	105-107	
12.	5.2	10.2	NG 5		58-60	108-110	
13.	5.3	10.3	NG 3		61-63	111-113	
14.	5.4	10.4	NG 14		64-66	114-116	
15.	5.5	10.5	NG 10		67-69	117-119	
16.	5.2	10.2	NG 4, 14		58-60	108-110	
17.	5.3	10.3	NG 9, 10, 13		61-63	111-113	
18.	5.4	10.4	NG 9, 13		64-66	114-116	
19.	5.4	10.4	12		64-66	114-116	
20.	5.5	10.5	12, 13		67-69	117-119	

Report Sheet

Latin America Benchmark Test 1

Overall Score _____

Question	Chapter/Section		Standard	Needs Review	Reading and Vocabulary Study Guide pages		Completed
	Latin America	Western Hemisphere			Latin America	Western Hemisphere	
1.	1.1	11.1	NG 2, 3		6-8	122-124	
2.	1.1	11.1	NG 2, 4		6-8	122-124	
3.	1.1	11.1	NG 2		6-8	122-124	
4.	1.2	11.2	NG 4, 11, 15		9-11	125-127	
5.	1.3	11.3	NG 11, 15, 16		12-14	128-130	
6.	1.3	11.3	NG 4		12-14	128-130	
7.	1.3	11.3	NG 1, 3, 9		12-14	128-130	
8.	1.3	11.3	NG 4, 9, 15, 18		12-14	128-130	
9.	1.3	11.3	NG 11		12-14	128-130	
10.	2.1	12.1	NG 12, 13		16-18	132-134	
11.	2.2	12.2	NG 4, 17		19-21	135-137	
12.	2.3	12.3	NG 9, 13		22-24	138-140	
13.	2.4	12.4	NG 13		25-27	141-143	
14.	2.4	12.4	NG 13		25-27	141-143	
15.	2.4	12.4	NG 13		25-27	141-143	
16.	3.1	13.1	NG 9		32-34	148-150	
17.	3.2	13.2	NG 9, 10		35-37	151-153	
18.	3.2	13.2	NG 9, 10		35-37	151-153	
19.	3.3	13.3	NG 11, 16		38-40	154-156	
20.	3.3	13.3	NG 10		38-40	154-156	

Report Sheet

Latin America Benchmark Test 2

Overall Score _____

Question	Chapter/Section		Standard	Needs Review	Reading and Vocabulary Study Guide pages		Completed
	Latin America	Western Hemisphere			Latin America	Western Hemisphere	
1.	4.1	14.1	NG 4, 9, 12		42-44	158-160	
2.	4.1	14.1	NG 4, 14		42-44	158-160	
3.	4.2	14.2	NG 4, 10		45-47	161-163	
4.	4.2	14.2	NG 10		45-47	161-163	
5.	4.3	14.3	NG 2		48-50	164-166	
6.	4.3	14.3	NG 11, 14		48-50	164-166	
7.	4.3	14.3	NG 13		48-50	164-166	
8.	5.1	15.1	NG 13		52-54	168-170	
9.	5.1	15.1	NG 13		52-54	168-170	
10.	5.2	15.2	NG 13		55-57	171-173	
11.	5.2	15.2	NG 4, 14		55-57	171-173	
12.	5.2	15.2	NG 2		55-57	171-173	
13.	5.3	15.3	NG 5, 13		58-60	174-176	
14.	5.3	15.3	NG 4, 6, 9, 10		58-60	174-176	
15.	6.1	16.1	NG 3, 4, 9, 12, 15, 18		62-64	178-180	
16.	6.1	16.1	NG 3, 4, 8, 9, 12, 14		62-64	178-180	
17.	6.1	16.1	NG 10, 12, 13, 15		62-64	178-180	
18.	6.2	16.2	NG 3, 4		65-67	181-183	
19.	6.3	16.3	NG 11, 16		68-70	184-186	
20.	6.4	16.4	NG 11, 16		71-73	187-189	

Name _____ Class _____ Date_____

Report Sheet

Europe and Russia Benchmark Test 1

Overall Score _____

Question	Chapter/Section		Standard	Needs Review	Reading and Vocabulary Study Guide pages		Completed
	Europe and Russia	Eastern Hemisphere			Europe and Russia	Eastern Hemisphere	
1.	1.1	6.1	NG 2		6-8	56-58	
2.	1.1	6.1	NG 5		6-8	56-58	
3.	1.1	6.1	NG 3		6-8	56-58	
4.	1.2	6.2	NG 8, 15		9-11	59-61	
5.	2.1	7.1	NG 12		16-18	66-68	
6.	2.1	7.1	NG 12		16-18	66-68	
7.	2.1	7.1	NG 13		16-18	66-68	
8.	1.3	6.3	NG 1		12-14	62-64	
9.	1.3	6.3	NG 1		12-14	62-64	
10.	2.2	7.2	NG 13		19-21	69-71	
11.	2.3	7.3	NG 11		22-24	72-74	
12.	2.4	7.4	NG 13		25-27	75-77	
13.	2.4	7.4	NG 10		25-27	75-77	
14.	2.4	7.4	NG 13		25-27	75-77	
15.	2.5	7.5	NG 12		28-30	78-80	
16.	3.1	8.1	NG 16, 11		32-34	82-84	
17.	3.2	8.2	NG 9, 10		35-37	85-87	
18.	3.3	8.3	NG 9, 10		38-40	88-90	
19.	3.2	8.2	NG 13		35-37	85-87	
20.	3.1	8.1	NG 9		32-34	82-84	

Report Sheet

Europe and Russia Benchmark Test 2

Overall Score _____

Question	Chapter/Section		Standard	Needs Review	Reading and Vocabulary Study Guide pages		Completed
	Europe and Russia	Eastern Hemisphere			Europe and Russia	Eastern Hemisphere	
1.	4.1	9.1	NG 4		42-44	92-94	
2.	4.1	9.1	NG 10		42-44	92-94	
3.	4.1	9.1	NG 4		42-44	92-94	
4.	4.2	9.2	NG 10		45-47	95-97	
5.	4.3	9.3	NG 15, 18		48-50	98-100	
6.	4.4	9.4	NG 4		51-53	101-103	
7.	4.4	9.4	NG 13		51-53	101-103	
8.	4.2	9.2	NG 9		45-47	95-97	
9.	4.3	9.3	NG 11		48-50	98-100	
10.	4.4	9.4	NG 16		51-53	101-103	
11.	4.5	9.5	NG 13		54-56	104-106	
12.	5.1	10.1	NG 13		58-60	108-110	
13.	5.1	10.1	NG 4		58-60	108-110	
14.	5.2	10.2	NG 13		61-63	111-113	
15.	5.2	10.2	NG 13		61-63	111-113	
16.	5.2	10.2	NG 11		61-63	111-113	
17.	5.3	10.3	NG 17		64-66	114-116	
18.	5.3	10.3	NG 6, 14		64-66	114-116	
19.	5.4	10.4	NG 11		67-69	117-119	
20.	5.4	10.4	NG 11		67-69	117-119	

Name _____ Class _____ Date_____

Report Sheet

Africa Benchmark Test 1

Overall Score _____

Question	Chapter/Section		Standard	Needs Review	Reading and Vocabulary Study Guide pages		Completed
	Africa	Eastern Hemisphere			Africa	Eastern Hemisphere	
1.	1.1	11.1	NG 2		6-8	122-124	
2.	1.1	11.1	NG 2		6-8	122-124	
3.	1.2	11.2	NG 8		9-11	125-127	
4.	1.3	11.3	NG 11		12-14	128-130	
5.	1.3	11.3	NG 11, 12		12-14	128-130	
6.	2.1	12.1	NG 9, 14		16-18	132-134	
7.	2.1	12.2	NG 10		16-18	135-137	
8.	1.2	11.2	NG 1, 4		9-11	125-127	
9.	2.2	12.2	NG 13		19-21	135-137	
10.	2.3	12.3	NG 13		22-24	138-140	
11.	2.3	12.3	NG 9,13		22-24	138-140	
12.	2.4	12.4	NG 13		25-27	141-143	
13.	2.5	12.5	NG 14		28-30	144-146	
14.	3.1	13.1	NG 10		30-34	148-150	
15.	3.2	13.2	NG 10		35-37	151-153	
16.	3.2	13.2	NG 9, 10		35-37	151-153	
17.	3.3	13.3	NG 10		38-40	154-156	
18.	3.4	13.4	NG 13		41-43	157-159	
19.	3.4	13.4	NG 4, 10		41-43	157-159	
20.	3.4	13.4	NG 4		41-43	157-159	

Report Sheet

Africa Benchmark Test 2

Overall Score _____

Question	Chapter/Section		Standard	Needs Review	Reading and Vocabulary Study Guide pages		Completed
	Africa	Eastern Hemisphere			Africa	Eastern Hemisphere	
1.	4.1	14.1	NG 10, 11, 12		45-47	161-163	
2.	4.1	14.1	NG 10		45-47	161-163	
3.	4.1	14.1	NG 14		45-47	161-163	
4.	4.2	14.2	NG 10		48-50	164-166	
5.	5.1	15.1	NG 4, 10		52-54	168-170	
6.	5.1	15.1	NG 13		52-54	168-170	
7.	5.1	15.1	NG 10		52-54	168-170	
8.	5.2	15.2	NG 11, 13		55-57	171-173	
9.	5.3	15.3	NG 14		58-60	174-176	
10.	5.3	15.3	NG 4, 8		58-60	174-176	
11.	6.1	16.1	NG 10		62-64	178-180	
12.	6.2	16.2	NG 12, 13		65-67	181-183	
13.	6.3	16.3	NG 10		68-70	184-186	
14.	6.3	16.3	NG 10		68-70	184-186	
15.	7.1	17.1	NG 11, 13		72-74	188-190	
16.	7.1	17.1	NG 13		72-74	188-190	
17.	7.1	17.1	NG 13		72-74	188-190	
18.	7.2	17.2	NG 10, 13		75-77	191-193	
19.	7.2	17.2	NG 13		75-77	191-193	
20.	7.2	17.2	NG 13		75-77	191-193	

Report Sheet

Asia and the Pacific Benchmark Test 1

Overall Score _____

Question	Chapter/Section		Standard	Needs Review	Reading and Vocabulary Study Guide pages		Completed
	Asia and the Pacific	Eastern Hemisphere			Asia and the Pacific	Eastern Hemisphere	
1.	1.1	18.1	NG 2, 4		6-8	196-198	
2.	1.3	18.3	NG 4, 14		12-14	202-204	
3.	2.1	19.1	NG 7		16-18	206-208	
4.	2.1	19.1	NG 4		16-18	206-208	
5.	2.1	19.1	NG 1, 9		16-18	206-208	
6.	2.1	19.1	NG 1, 4		16-18	206-208	
7.	3.1	20.1	NG 15		26-28	216-218	
8.	2.2	19.2	NG 15		19-21	209-211	
9.	3.1	20.1	NG 2, 5		26-28	216-218	
10.	3.2	20.2	NG 8		29-31	219-221	
11.	3.2	20.2	NG 3, 9		29-31	219-221	
12.	3.2	20.2	NG 4, 15		29-31	219-221	
13.	3.3	20.3	NG 7		32-34	222-224	
14.	3.3	20.3	NG 9, 12		32-34	222-224	
15.	3.3	20.3	NG 11		32-34	222-224	
16.	2.1	19.1	NG 2, 4		16-18	206-208	
17.	2.2	19.2	NG 11, 15		19-21	209-211	
18.	1.3	18.3	NG 15		12-14	202-204	
19.	1.2	18.2	NG 15		10-13	199-201	
20.	1.3	18.3	NG 11, 13		26-28	202-204	

Report Sheet

Asia and the Pacific Benchmark Test 2

Overall Score _____

Question	Chapter/Section		Standard	Needs Review	Reading and Vocabulary Study Guide pages		Completed
	Asia and the Pacific	Eastern Hemisphere			Asia and the Pacific	Eastern Hemisphere	
1.	4.1	21.1	NG 4, 10		36-38	226-228	
2.	4.2	21.2	NG 12		39-41	229-231	
3.	5.1	22.1	NG 10		43-45	233-235	
4.	4.2	21.2	NG 10		39-41	229-231	
5.	4.2	21.2	NG 6, 10		39-41	229-231	
6.	5.2	22.2	NG 12		46-48	232-234	
7.	5.2	22.2	NG 15		46-48	232-234	
8.	5.2	22.2	NG 13		46-48	232-234	
9.	6.1	23.1	NG 13		53-55	243-245	
10.	6.1	23.1	NG 13		53-55	243-245	
11.	6.1	23.1	NG 13		53-55	243-245	
12.	6.2	23.2	NG 13		56-58	246-248	
13.	6.2	23.2	NG 12		56-58	246-248	
14.	6.2	23.2	NG 13		56-58	246-248	
15.	4.1	21.1	NG 13		36-38	226-228	
16.	5.1	22.1	NG 10, 13		43-45	226-228	
17.	5.3	22.3	NG 4, 10		49-51	239-241	
18.	5.2	22.2	NG 6, 10, 13		46-48	236-238	
19.	6.2	23.2	NG 9, 17		56-58	246-248	
20.	6.2	23.2	NG 10		56-58	246-248	

Report Sheet

Asia and the Pacific Benchmark Test 3

Overall Score _____

Question	Chapter/Section		Standard	Needs Review	Reading and Vocabulary Study Guide pages		Completed
	Asia and the Pacific	Eastern Hemisphere			Asia and the Pacific	Eastern Hemisphere	
1.	7.1	24.1	NG 11, 13		60-62	250-252	
2.	7.1	24.1	NG 11, 13		60-62	250-252	
3.	7.2	24.2	NG 11, 13		63-65	253-255	
4.	7.3	24.3	NG 13		66-68	256-258	
5.	7.3	24.3	NG 11, 13		66-68	256-258	
6.	8.1	25.1	NG 12, 13		70-72	260-262	
7.	8.2	25.2	NG 1		73-75	263-265	
8.	8.2	25.2	NG 4, 11		73-75	263-265	
9.	8.4	25.4	NG 10		79-81	269-271	
10.	8.5	25.5	NG 14		82-84	272-274	
11.	9.1	26.1	NG 13		86-88	276-278	
12.	9.1	26.1	NG 14		86-88	276-278	
13.	9.2	26.2	NG 11		89-91	279-281	
14.	9.2	26.2	NG 11		89-91	279-281	
15.	9.2	26.2	NG 4, 11		89-91	279-281	
16.	7.2	24.2	NG 9		63-65	253-255	
17.	8.3	25.3	NG 14		76-78	266-268	
18.	8.3	25.3	NG 10, 13		76-78	266-268	
19.	8.4	25.4	NG 4, 11, 15, 16		79-81	269-271	
20.	8.5	25.5	NG 2, 11, 15		82-84	272-274	

Report Sheet

The Ancient World Benchmark Test 1

Overall Score _____

Question	Chapter/ Section	Standard	Needs Review	Reading and Vocabulary Study Guide pages	Completed
1.	1.1	NG 6		6-8	
2.	1.2	NG 12		9-11	
3.	1.2	NG 12		9-11	
4.	1.3	NG 12		12-14	
5.	2.1	NG 8		16-18	
6.	2.2	NG 10		19-21	
7.	2.3	NG 12, 13		22-24	
8.	2.4	NG 12		25-27	
9.	2.4	NG 10		25-27	
10.	2.5	NG 10		28-30	
11.	3.2	NG 4, 13		35-37	
12.	3.5	NG 13		44-46	
13.	4.1	NG 2,4		48-50	
14.	4.1	NG 12, 13		48-50	
15.	4.2	NG 10		51-53	
16.	2.3	NG 12, 13		16-18	
17.	2.3	NG 12, 13		16-18	
18.	3.2	NG 12, 13		35-37	
19.	3.2	NG 12		35-37	
20.	4.4	NG 10, 13		57-59	

Report Sheet

The Ancient World Benchmark Test 2

Overall Score _____

Question	Chapter/ Section	Standard	Needs Review	Reading and Vocabulary Study Guide pages	Completed
1.	5.1	NG 4		61–63	
2.	5.1	NG 4, 10		61–63	
3.	5.2	NG 4, 13		64–66	
4.	5.3	NG 11		67–69	
5.	5.3	NG 13		67–69	
6.	5.4	NG 10, 11		71–73	
7.	5.4	NG 4, 12		71–73	
8.	6.1	NG 2, 4		74–76	
9.	6.1	NG 4, 10		74–76	
10.	6.1	NG 4, 13		74–76	
11.	6.1	NG 12, 13		74–76	
12.	6.2	NG 4		77–79	
13.	6.4	NG 4, 13		83–85	
14.	7.1	NG 1		90–92	
15.	7.1	NG 13		90–92	
16.	6.3	NG 4, 13		80–82	
17.	7.2	NG 10		93–95	
18.	7.3	NG 4, 12		96–98	
19.	7.4	NG 4, 10, 13		99–101	
20.	7.5	NG 11, 13		102–104	

Report Sheet

Medieval Times to Today Benchmark Test 1

Overall Score _____

Question	Chapter/ Section	Standard	Needs Review	Reading and Vocabulary Study Guide pages	Completed
1.	1.1	NG 1, 5		6-8	
2.	1.1	NG 10		6-8	
3.	1.2	NG 10		6-8	
4.	1.3	NG 10		12-14	
5.	2.1	NG 10, 12, 16		19-21	
6.	2.2	NG 11, 16		22-24	
7.	2.2	NG 11, 16, 17		22-24	
8.	2.2	NG 2		22-24	
9.	1.3	NG 2, 3		12-14	
10.	3.3	NG 1		35-37	
11.	3.1	NG 3, 15, 17		29-31	
12.	3.2	NG 7, 14		32-34	
13.	4.1	NG 4, 14		39-41	
14.	4.3	NG 10		45-47	
15.	4.1	NG 10		39-41	
16.	1.3	NG 10		12-14	
17.	2.3	NG 11		25-27	
18.	3.1	NG 13		29-31	
19.	3.2	NG 12		32-34	
20.	4.2	NG 16		42-44	

Name_____ Class_____ Date_____

Report Sheet

Medieval Times to Today Benchmark Test 2

Overall Score _____

Question	Chapter/ Section	Standard	Needs Review	Reading and Vocabulary Study Guide pages	Completed
1.	5.2	NG 3, 17		52-54	
2.	5.1	NG 12		49-51	
3.	5.2	NG 12		52-54	
4.	5.3	NG 13		55-57	
5.	5.4	NG 12		58-60	
6.	6.1	NG 15		62-64	
7.	7.2	NG 13		65-67	
8.	6.3	NG 16		68-70	
9.	6.3	NG 10		68-70	
10.	6.4	NG 16		71-73	
11.	6.4	NG 4, 9		71-73	
12.	7.1	NG 13		75-77	
13.	7.2	NG 13		78-80	
14.	7.2	NG 13		78-80	
15.	7.3	NG 11		81-83	
16.	7.4	NG 16		84-86	
17.	8.1	NG 16		88-90	
18.	8.2	NG 2, 13		91-93	
19.	8.2	NG 11		91-93	
20.	8.3	NG 11		94-96	

Name _____ Class _____ Date_____

Foundations of Geography Outcome Test

Directions: *Read each question and choose the best answer. Then mark the letter for the answer you have chosen.*

1. What do geographers learn by studying the theme of human-environment interaction?

   A. how people move from one region to another

   B. how cultural features define a location

   C. how people and the environment affect each other

   D. how regions differ from each other

2. What problem limits the usefulness of globes?

   A. Globes are created using flat maps, so the world is not shown to scale.

   B. Globes cannot be detailed to be useful and at the same time be small enough to be convenient.

   C. A globe is not the same shape as Earth.

   D. It is impossible to show Earth on a round surface without distortion.

3. What creates a change in seasons?

   A. Earth tilts on its axis and orbits the sun.

   B. Earth reverses the direction of its rotation every three months.

   C. Earth rotates on its axis.

   D. The moon rotates around the Earth.

4. Which of the following is a physical process that mainly occurs outside the Earth's surface?

   A. volcanoes   C. shifting plates

   B. earthquakes   D. erosion

5. What role does the atmosphere play in the natural resources needed for life?

   A. It limits the production of saltwater that evaporates from the ocean's surface, so that more fresh water remains.

   B. It creates weathering, which helps build Earth's largest landforms from tiny pieces of rock and plant material.

   C. It provides life-giving oxygen for people and animals and provides carbon dioxide for plants.

   D. It releases the heat of Earth into space, allowing Earth to cool enough to support life.

6. Imagine a map of North America with colors that show temperatures on a day in winter. The colors are shaded from light to dark, with light representing the warmest temperatures and dark representing the coldest temperatures. How does the shade around a city on the coast compare to the shade around an inland city at the same latitude?

   A. The two areas are exactly the same shade.

   B. The two areas are nearly the same shade.

   C. The shade of the city on the coast is lighter.

   D. The shade of the city on the coast is darker.

Foundations of Geography Outcome Test *(continued)*

7. Which of the following reasons BEST explains the high population growth in the United States today?
   A. Farm families are given a special tax credit to have more children.
   B. The number of births each year equals the number of deaths.
   C. New farming methods have greatly increased the food supply.
   D. Average life expectancy has decreased in the last 50 years.

8. In the past, why did most people settle in areas with rich soil and good sources of water?
   A. Most people grew their own food.
   B. Most people enjoyed rural life.
   C. Most people wanted to be near a big city.
   D. Most people worked on rivers and lakes.

9. Which process accounts for the cultural diversity of North America?
   A. urbanization
   B. immigration
   C. migration loss
   D. population loss

10. Which of the following is a greater problem in developed nations than in developing nations?
    A. food shortages
    B. unsafe water
    C. pollution
    D. disease

11. The particular way in which farmers from different cultures lay out their fields is an example of
    A. cultural landscape.
    B. cultural traits.
    C. acculturation.
    D. cultural diffusion.

12. What can be concluded about the people of a country if the population speaks more than one language?
    A. The people all have the same culture.
    B. There are some cultural differences among the people.
    C. The process of cultural diffusion is incomplete among those people.
    D. The process of urbanization is incomplete among those people.

13. How are energy resources spread around the world?
    A. All countries have enough energy resources to meet their own energy needs.
    B. Not all countries need energy.
    C. All countries need energy, and some have to buy energy from other countries.
    D. All countries have the same energy needs and the same energy resources.

14. Manufacturing is an example of a
    A. first-level economic activity.
    B. second-level economic activity.
    C. third-level economic activity.
    D. fourth-level economic activity.

Foundations of Geography Outcome Test *(continued)*

15. How does deforestation affect the ecosystem?

   A. It creates farmland that helps feed many people and strengthens the ecosystem.

   B. It destroys the homes of many plants and animals and may result in a loss of biodiversity.

   C. It destroys the atmosphere's ozone layer but replenishes algae and plant life in lakes and rivers.

   D. It reduces the world's human population, pollutes water, and increases the oxygen content in the air.

16. Because many of Earth's resources are limited, people will have to

   A. use available resources now, before they run out.

   B. reduce their use of limited resources.

   C. find new sources of air and water pollution.

   D. stop using solar power and wind power.

17. The United Kingdom and the Netherlands are examples of a

   A. representative democracy.

   B. absolute monarchy.

   C. direct democracy.

   D. constitutional monarchy.

18. How are countries classified as developed or developing?

   A. by number of cities and population

   B. by number of industries and level of technological advancement

   C. by amount of energy resources

   D. by how much money the country makes each year

19. Which statement BEST describes the relationship between developed and developing nations?

   A. Developed nations depend on developing nations for natural resources and simple industrial products.

   B. Developing nations sell high technology products to developed nations.

   C. Developed nations sell food and oil to developing nations.

   D. Developing nations are not interested in the products of developing nations.

20. The development of early cultures included four major advances in technology. They are the invention of tools, control of fire, beginning of agriculture, and

   A. complex institutions.

   B. development of civilizations.

   C. institutions of higher learning.

   D. the Green Revolution.

Foundations of Geography Outcome Test (continued)

Directions: *Read each question. Write your response on the lines provided.*

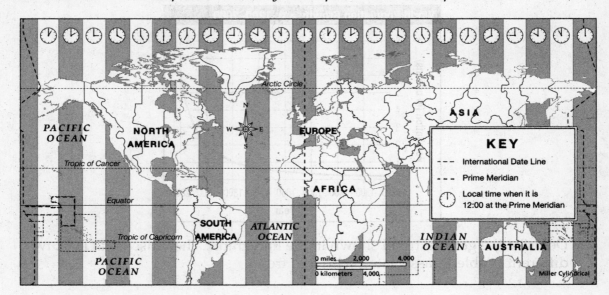

21. Explain the time zones shown on the map. Why are they necessary? How do they help avoid confusion?

_____

_____

_____

_____

22. Describe two different ways natural forces shape Earth's surface.

_____

_____

_____

_____

_____

Foundations of Geography Outcome Test (continued)

World Population Growth, A.D. 1200–2000

23. Describe the general trend shown in the line graph. Then discuss at least two different problems associated with that trend.

_____

_____

_____

_____

24. Select two of the types of government listed, and write a brief description of each: direct democracy, tribal rule, absolute monarchy, dictatorship, oligarchy, constitutional monarchy, representative democracy.

_____

_____

_____

_____

Foundations of Geography Outcome Test (continued)

25. In an essay, describe the way people use the world's natural resources. You may want to consider renewable and nonrenewable resources.

_____

_____

_____

_____

_____

_____

_____

_____

_____

_____

_____

_____

_____

_____

_____

_____

_____

_____

_____

_____

_____

_____

_____

_____

The United States and Canada Outcome Test

Directions: *Read each question and choose the best answer. Then mark the letter for the answer you have chosen.*

1. Which is the largest mountain system in North America?
   A. Appalachian Mountains
   B. Rocky Mountains
   C. Sierra Nevada Mountains
   D. Cascade Mountains

2. How do volcanoes produce mountains?
   A. Molten rock breaks through the Earth's crust.
   B. Slow-moving sheets of ice cut away mountainsides.
   C. Rushing water creates valleys, dividing land into mountains.
   D. Steaming water breaks through the Earth's crust.

3. Most people who live in the tundra make their living by
   A. logging.
   B. growing wheat and other crops.
   C. raising cattle and sheep.
   D. fishing and hunting.

4. In 1754 Britain and France went to war. Who helped the British soldiers defeat the French?
   A. Native Americans
   B. the colonists
   C. Spanish soldiers
   D. Mexican soldiers

5. The United States economy _____ right after World War I.
   A. showed a slight decline
   B. improved gradually
   C. remained unchanged
   D. boomed

6. How did the admission of California to the Union add to the conflict about slavery that eventually led to the Civil War?
   A. It encouraged slave owners to move to California.
   B. It upset the balance of states in the west and states in the east.
   C. It upset the balance of free states and slave states.
   D. It allowed people to start gold mines in California.

7. In 1867 Canada became a dominion, which meant that it was
   A. completely independent.
   B. completely dependent.
   C. self-governing but not independent.
   D. independent but not self-governing.

8. What are the United States and Canada trying to do about forests and the timber industry?
   A. The United States maintains forests, and Canada maintains the timber industry.
   B. Canada is trying to maintain forests, and the United States is trying to maintain the timber industry.
   C. Both are trying to maintain forests, even if the timber industry is destroyed.
   D. Both are trying to maintain both their forests and timber industry.

The United States and Canada Outcome Test (continued)

9. The first groups in North America to be involved in a cultural exchange were
   - A. different Native American groups with each other.
   - B. Spanish and French explorers with each other.
   - C. Spanish and French explorers with Native Americans.
   - D. English settlers with Native Americans.

10. During the Industrial Revolution, new technology, such as the steamboat and railroad, improved transportation. What effect did this have on the United States?
    - A. Transporting people and goods around the United States became faster and easier.
    - B. The United States was able to wage war against Canada.
    - C. Expensive improvements crippled the economy.
    - D. It had very little impact on the United States.

11. Why is its warm climate important to the economy of the South?
    - A. The climate keeps immigrants from moving to the South.
    - B. The climate helps make it easier to grow crops and raise animals.
    - C. The climate helps keep tourists away from the South.
    - D. The climate helps keep boll weevils alive.

12. How has the rise of corporate farms affected employment possibilities for farm workers in the Midwest?
    - A. Corporate farms employ about the same number of farm workers as family farms.
    - B. Corporate farms employ more farm workers than family farms.
    - C. Corporate farms employ fewer farm workers than family farms.
    - D. Corporate farms do not employ any farm workers at all.

13. Why did San Francisco, California, grow so quickly from 1848 to 1850?
    - A. Gold was discovered in San Francisco.
    - B. Tourists came to San Francisco on their way to visit the first national parks.
    - C. Workers came to San Francisco to build dams and hydroelectric plants.
    - D. Miners and prospectors stopped in San Francisco to buy supplies before heading off to the mountains to look for gold.

14. Who are Canadian separatists?
    - A. people who want Canada to be separate from Great Britain
    - B. people who want Canadian culture to be more clearly different from the culture of the United States
    - C. people who want Canada to separate into five smaller countries
    - D. people who want Quebec to break away from Canada and become an independent country

The United States and Canada Outcome Test (continued)

15. Which sentence best explains the attitudes of native peoples and settlers of European descent toward buffalo in the Prairie Provinces?

   A. The native peoples depended on the buffalo for survival, but used only what they needed. People of European descent wanted to sell buffalo hides and hunt buffalo for sport.

   B. Both the native peoples and the people of European descent depended on the buffalo for survival.

   C. Both the native peoples and the people of European descent wanted to sell buffalo hides and hunt buffalo for sport.

   D. The people of European descent depended on the buffalo for survival, but the native peoples wanted to sell buffalo hides and hunt buffalo for sport.

16. How are the northern territories different from the provinces of Canada?

   A. The territories are closer to the equator.

   B. The territories have larger populations than most of the provinces do.

   C. The territories are not controlled by the federal government, and the provinces are.

   D. The federal government has more control over the territories than it does over the provinces.

17. Canada's newest territory was created in 1999. Most residents are Inuit. The territory is called

   A. Inuktitut.

   B. Halifax.

   C. Saskatchewan.

   D. Nunavut.

18. Where is the Sun Belt located?

   A. It stretches from the southern Atlantic Coast to the coast of California.

   B. It is located at the narrowest point across Florida.

   C. It is the Canadian name for the United States/Canada border.

   D. It is located in the heart of Texas.

19. Chicago, Detroit and St. Louis, Missouri are examples of Midwest cities that began as

   A. European colonies.

   B. centers of transportation and processing used by farmers.

   C. corporate farms.

   D. boomtowns with a growing population of miners.

20. Mountains separating British Columbia and the rest of Canada have resulted in a link between British Columbia and

   A. the United States.

   B. the Atlantic Province.

   C. the Pacific Rim.

   D. Mexico, the Caribbean, and Middle America.

The United States and Canada Outcome Test (continued)

Directions: *Read each question. Write your response on the lines provided.*

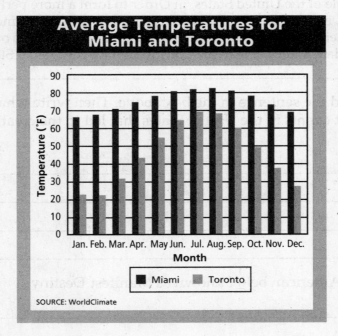

21. Summarize the information presented in the graph, and describe how these temperature variations probably affect the lives of people in Miami and Toronto.

_____

_____

_____

_____

22. Compare the governments of the United States and Canada. How are they alike? How are they different?

_____

_____

_____

_____

The United States and Canada Outcome Test (continued)

> We the People of the United States, in Order to form a more perfect Union, establish Justice, insure domestic Tranquility, provide for the common defense, promote the general Welfare, and secure the Blessings of Liberty to ourselves and our Posterity, do ordain and establish this Constitution for the United States of America.

23. Carefully read the sentence in the box above. Then write what you have learned about events in the United States that led to the creation of this document.

_____

_____

_____

_____

24. Describe the American belief known as Manifest Destiny.

_____

_____

_____

The United States and Canada Outcome Test (continued)

25. A section in your book is entitled <u>The United States: A Nation of Immigrants</u>. Write an essay describing the ways the United States has benefited from a variety of people. Include some of the challenges immigrants face as they adapt to a new culture.

_____

_____

_____

_____

_____

_____

_____

_____

_____

_____

_____

_____

_____

_____

_____

_____

_____

_____

_____

_____

_____

Latin America Outcome Test

Directions: *Read each question and choose the best answer. Then mark the letter for the answer you have chosen.*

1. Some of the Caribbean Islands were formed by
   - A. the melding together of the skeletons of sea animals.
   - B. the joining together of Totora reeds.
   - C. the flooding of lowlands surrounding a mountain range.
   - D. the joining together of smaller islands.

2. In Latin America, snow is found year-round above an elevation of 14,000 feet. This elevation is referred to as the Snow Line. The Tree Line is the line below the Snow Line. What would you find at elevations between the Tree Line and the Snow Line?
   - A. crops such as apples and wheat
   - B. trees
   - C. crops such as bananas and rice
   - D. growth that supports grazing

3. Weather can affect natural resources and industries. Which effect might El Niño cause?
   - A. It brings plant diseases that destroy crops.
   - B. It brings warm water, which kills the plants on which fish feed, causing them to move to other areas.
   - C. It brings cold water, which attracts fish to the area, creating a benefit for the fishing industry.
   - D. It brings snow to lower elevations, which destroys crops.

4. Which of the following were conquered by Spanish conquistadors who came to Latin America?
   - A. Aztecs, Criollos
   - B. Incas, Criollos
   - C. Aztecs, Incas
   - D. Mayas, Criollos

5. Without the use of modern tools, Incan stoneworkers were able to build
   - A. only very small buildings.
   - B. beautiful buildings that were weak in structure.
   - C. lasting buildings without the use of mortar or cement.
   - D. structures with brick and mud.

6. Why did European explorers come to the Americas in the 1400s and 1500s?
   - A. They wanted to establish diplomatic relations.
   - B. They were interested in learning about Native American culture.
   - C. They hoped to find gold and other treasures there.
   - D. They wanted to find slaves to bring back to Europe.

7. About 30 percent of the people of Mexico are indigenous, and about 60 percent are mestizos. Assuming these figures are correct, about what percent of the population of Mexico have Native American ancestors?
   - A. 10 percent
   - B. 30 percent
   - C. 60 percent
   - D. 90 percent

Latin America Outcome Test (continued)

8. Which of the following is a factor that led to ethnic variety in the Caribbean?

   A. Many inhabitants came as colonists, slaves, or immigrants.

   B. The wide variety of religious beliefs has created a diverse culture.

   C. Internal political struggles continually erupt in the government.

   D. People were drawn by opportunities in the gold mining industry.

9. Which statement BEST describes the role of women in South America?

   A. Women have fewer opportunities than men, but are largely accepting of this due to cultural custom.

   B. Women do not yet play an equal role, but are fighting for more rights.

   C. Women and men play relatively equal roles.

   D. Women are less likely than men to be poor, due to laws of inheritance in South America, and this has allowed them to play an important role in everyday life.

Directions: *Use the map <u>and</u> your knowledge of social studies to answer question 10.*

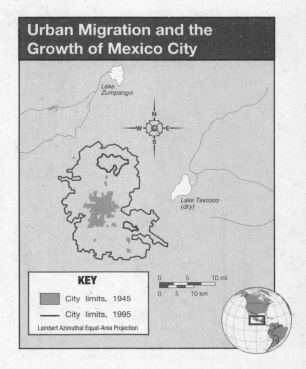

10. Look at the Urban Migration and the Growth of Mexico City map. Which of the following statements BEST describes what is shown on this map?

   A. In 1995, the population of Mexico City had decreased to one tenth of its size in 1945.

   B. Since 1945, most people have migrated from Mexico City to its surrounding areas.

   C. Mexico City covers more than twice the land than it did in 1945.

   D. Since 1945, most people who live in Mexico City are farmers.

Latin America Outcome Test (continued)

Use the map __and__ your knowledge of social studies to answer question 11.

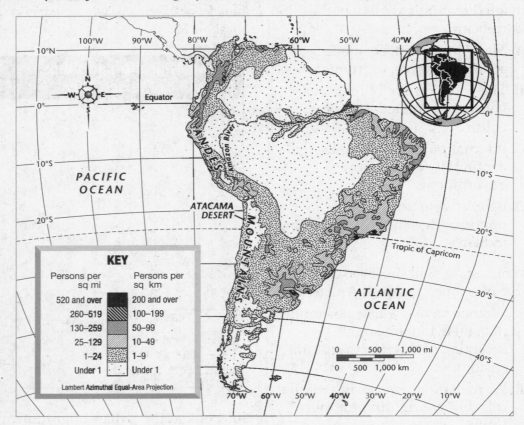

11. Which of the following is MOST LIKELY to be true of Brazil?

   A. Brazil's rain forest is located along the coast.

   B. The interior is highly developed.

   C. Cities are more culturally diverse than interior areas.

   D. Brazil's people tend to live far from water sources.

12. Land reform is the effort to

   A. save land from overuse.

   B. distribute land more equally among people.

   C. rezone land for industrial use.

   D. rezone land for agricultural use.

13. One reason many Cubans left their homeland after Castro came to power is

   A. the struggling economy made necessities scarce.

   B. they were ordered to leave.

   C. the extreme weather conditions made life too difficult.

   D. parents felt their children could not get a basic education there.

14. In 1990, Jean-Bertrand Aristide was

   A. the first democratically elected president of Haiti.

   B. a Mexican artist whose work shows the struggle for freedom.

   C. a Chilean poet who won the Nobel Prize.

   D. Fidel Castro's replacement.

Latin America Outcome Test (continued)

15. Knowing where Puerto Rico is situated, and that its crops include sugar cane and citrus fruits, what can you say about its climate?

A. Its climate is arid.

B. Its climate is cool and rainy.

C. Its climate is similar to that of southern South America.

D. Its climate is warm and sunny.

16. The Amazon Basin is populated

A. by millions of people.

B. by millions of plant and animal species.

C. by few people, plants or animals, due to desert-like conditions.

D. largely by immigrants.

17. An example of how humans adapt to geographic factors in Peru is

A. Uros creating islands from reeds to increase the amount of usable land.

B. Native Americans leaving the Altiplano for the city.

C. indigenous groups dying from diseases brought by foreigners.

D. Incas using a census to count the people living in their cities.

18. The Strait of Magellan is

A. where Magellan first encountered Native Americans.

B. located near Panama.

C. a safer route for ships than going farther south around the Cape Horn.

D. the largest tributary of the Amazon River.

19. The Amazon River flows through which two countries?

A. Brazil and Bolivia

B. Brazil and Colombia

C. Brazil and Peru

D. Brazil and Uruguay

20. Which of the following helps to support Panama's economy today?

A. banking and finance, mining, ecotourism

B. ecotourism, mining, manufacturing

C. manufacturing, mining, banking and finance

D. banking and finance, ecotourism, manufacturing

Latin America Outcome Test *(continued)*

21. Briefly describe how geography shaped the history of the area that is now the nation of Panama.

_____

_____

_____

_____

22. Give a reason why the conquistadors were able to defeat the two most powerful empires in the Americas—the Aztecs and the Incas.

_____

_____

_____

_____

23. Describe the geography of Chile.

_____

_____

_____

_____

24. Describe the differences and similarities between Puerto Rico and the mainland United States.

_____

_____

_____

_____

Latin America Outcome Test (continued)

> We have lived in this place for a long time, a very long time, since the time when the world did not yet have this shape. We learned with the ancients that we are a tiny part of this immense universe, fellow travelers with all the animals, the plants, and the waters. We are all a part of the whole. We cannot neglect or destroy our home. And now we want to talk to those who cannot yet manage to see the world in this way, to say to them that together we have to take care of the boat in which we are all sailing.
>
> -Ailton Krenak, as quoted in *Rain Forest Amerindians* by Anna Lewington

25. Read the above quote from Ailton Krenak, an activist working to protect the rain forests of Brazil from development and to preserve the forests for the Amerindians living there. What effects of development of the rain forest does the author probably wish to avoid, and why?

_____

_____

_____

_____

_____

_____

_____

_____

_____

_____

_____

_____

_____

_____

_____

Europe and Russia Outcome Test

Directions: *Read each question and choose the best answer. Then mark the letter for the answer you have chosen.*

Use the population chart and your knowledge of social studies to answer questions 1-2.

Country	Population Density (Persons per Square Mile)
Albania	316
France	284
Germany	602
Italy	496
Poland	320
Russia	22
Sweden	51
Ukraine	209
United Kingdom	633
United States	75

1. Which of the following is reflected by the chart above?
   A. North Europe is less densely populated than south Europe.
   B. European countries are more densely populated than Russia and the United States.
   C. Eastern Europe is more densely populated than Western Europe.
   D. Countries of the former Soviet Union are more densely populated.

2. Which of the following greatly affects Russia's population density?
   A. The Ural Mountains form a barrier.
   B. Many people have moved to Russia from other countries.
   C. The huge area of Siberia has a harsh climate.
   D. The rivers in Siberia run north.

3. Who was Alexander the Great?
   A. the first Roman emperor to conquer lands and build roads
   B. a Greek king who fought against the Persians
   C. the king of Macedonia who spread the Greek culture as he set out to conquer the world
   D. a peasant who became emperor of Rome

4. The Roman Empire was divided into two parts because
   A. the eastern part didn't want to support Christianity.
   B. it was conquered by Mongols.
   C. it had become too big for one person to rule.
   D. the western part wanted to explore the Americas.

5. The system of feudalism during the Middle Ages involved
   A. nobles protecting the serfs who worked on their land.
   B. absolute monarchs who united their nations.
   C. nobles who were free of kings.
   D. small farms owned by peasants.

6. What was one reason for the Renaissance?
   A. European traders grew rich and had time for art and education.
   B. New inventions forced Europeans to reexamine the world.
   C. The Church encouraged scientific learning in schools.
   D. Europeans needed raw materials to produce manufactured goods.

Europe and Russia Outcome Test (continued)

Directions: *Use the map and your knowledge of social studies to answer questions 7-8.*

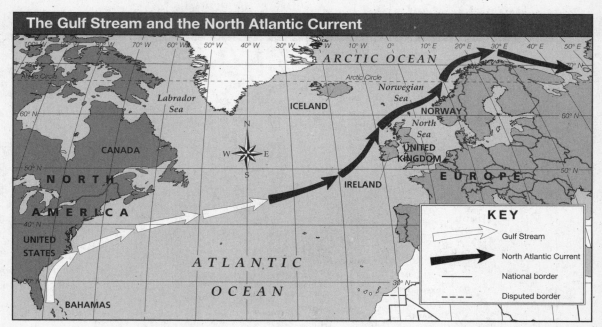

The Gulf Stream and the North Atlantic Current

7. Which describes the relationship between the Gulf Stream and the North Atlantic Current?

   A. The North Atlantic Current becomes the Gulf Stream after it crosses the Atlantic Ocean.

   B. Both are caused by cold water coming down from Iceland.

   C. They collide in the middle of the Atlantic Ocean.

   D. The Gulf Stream becomes the North Atlantic Current after it crosses the Atlantic Ocean.

8. What affect does the North Atlantic Current have on Western Europe?

   A. It causes Western Europe to be dry much of the year.

   B. It brings a milder climate with less rainfall.

   C. It brings a milder climate with more rainfall.

   D. It prevents many ports there from being used for shipping.

9. How did Sweden's economic troubles in the late 1800s affect the United States?

   A. Many Swedes left their country in search of a better life and moved to the United States.

   B. Sweden borrowed money from the United States and in return became a constitutional monarchy.

   C. Many Americans moved to Sweden to help rebuild Swedish industry.

   D. Tension began to grow when the United States refused to lend Sweden money.

10. Which of the following is the most common ethnic group in Poland, Croatia, Slovenia, and the Czech Republic?

   A. Serbs   C. Slavs

   B. Magyars   D. Roma

Europe and Russia Outcome Test *(continued)*

Use the map and your knowledge of social studies to answer questions 11-12.

European Union 1957-2004

KEY
Members by:
- 1957
- 1973
- 1986
- 2000
- 2004
- National border

11. Which of the following were original members of the European Union in 1957?

   A. Belgium, United Kingdom, Italy, the Netherlands

   B. France, Italy, the Netherlands, Greece

   C. France, Spain, Italy, Denmark

   D. Belgium, France, Italy, the Netherlands

12. Which of the following is a result of the European Union?

   A. All of the member countries are protected by fortifications along the Mediterranean Sea.

   B. There is a single set of laws for all of the member nations.

   C. A citizen of Spain can travel all the way to Denmark without a passport.

   D. Taxes are about the same in all the countries.

Europe and Russia Outcome Test (continued)

13. What was Winston Churchill referring to in his 1946 speech when he said "an iron curtain has descended across the Continent?"

A. the Berlin Wall

B. the split in Eastern and Western Europe between democracies and Communist countries

C. the ethnic conflicts which caused civil wars

D. the division between wealthy countries and poor countries

14. Why is the Magna Carta significant?

A. It was the first time a leader was elected by the people.

B. It limited the power of the king and led to Parliament.

C. It was the first declaration of independence.

D. For the first time, citizens gathered to discuss politics.

15. In the Soviet Union, education was

A. very expensive.

B. only offered to wealthy families.

C. taught in the home.

D. free.

16. How did Great Britain's location on a small island affect its economic development?

A. Isolated from other countries, it didn't develop as a trading country.

B. Limited natural resources made trade very important.

C. Poor farmland made it dependent on other countries.

D. Often invaded, it developed a variety of different industries.

17. Why did France encourage immigration after World War II?

A. It had a shortage of workers.

B. It wanted people to settle in some remote areas.

C. It wanted to blend French culture with other cultures.

D. It wanted a larger population to prevent another war.

18. Which of the following characterizes Sweden today?

A. People get very few services but pay low taxes.

B. It has efficient industries and people take few vacations.

C. People pay high taxes but get extensive services in return.

D. The north is very industrial and the south is more rural.

19. The breakup of Yugoslavia has

A. been largely peaceful.

B. been caused by economic problems.

C. prevented people from worshipping their own religions.

D. required the involvement of NATO and the UN to keep peace.

20. During communist control in Poland, coal and steel production was

A. stopped because they wanted greater agricultural production.

B. the cause of widespread pollution and the destruction of forests.

C. modern and is still among the world leaders in exports.

D. used to help the Soviet Union rebuild its army.

Europe and Russia Outcome Test (continued)

21. The Renaissance is often understood as the rebirth of interest in learning and art. Describe some examples of this interest in learning and art.

_____

_____

_____

_____

22. The reunification of Germany after the fall of communism brought significant challenges. Briefly describe these challenges and what the new government did to face them.

_____

_____

_____

_____

23. Although it had much rich farmland, many people in Ukraine starved during the 1930s. What were the conditions at the time and why did it happen?

_____

_____

_____

_____

24. "Democracy is the wholesome and pure air without which a socialist public organization cannot live a full-blooded life." Mikhail Gorbachev spoke these words to the Communist Party Congress in 1986 not long after he took power. He used the words "socialist public organization" to refer to the Communist government of the Soviet Union. Briefly describe the circumstances around that time and what changes Gorbachev was proposing.

_____

_____

_____

_____

Europe and Russia Outcome Test (continued)

25. The peoples of Eastern and Western Europe have had very different
experiences since the end of World War II. Write a short, three-paragraph essay
that compares the basic type of government, culture, and economy of each and
describes their prospects in the near future.

_____

_____

_____

_____

_____

_____

_____

_____

_____

_____

_____

_____

_____

_____

_____

_____

_____

_____

_____

_____

_____

_____

_____

_____

Africa Outcome Test

Directions: *Read each question and choose the best answer. Then mark the letter for the answer you have chosen.*

1. Africa has two major deserts. People who live in these deserts are
   A. few in number.
   B. likely to live in permanent settlements.
   C. usually farmers.
   D. called the Berbers.

2. Because the Equator runs through the midsection of Africa, the month of July is
   A. extremely hot and dry throughout every region of the continent.
   B. summer for the entire continent.
   C. summer for the countries in Northern Africa and winter in countries of Southern Africa.
   D. winter for the countries in Northern Africa and summer in countries of Southern Africa.

3. In 1324, Mansa Musa made a pilgrimage to Mecca, a Muslim holy place. In addition to his religious purpose, what else did Musa accomplish with this trip?
   A. He brought about new trading ties and displayed Mali's wealth.
   B. He brought about new trading ties with nations of Europe, but not with other Muslim nations.
   C. He brought about new trading ties by displaying Mali's poverty.
   D. He was not able to bring about new trading ties, but was able to display Mali's wealth.

4. About 4,000 years ago, Bantu people began one of the largest migrations that ever took place. Why did so many migrate?
   A. to escape drought and find food
   B. the reason is unknown, but an increased food supply may have caused overcrowding and the need for some to leave
   C. evidence shows that the Bantu people were conquered and forced to leave by a new ruler
   D. the reason for the migration is unknown, but most scientists agree that desertification had started where they were

5. How did the early kingdoms in West Africa become wealthy?
   A. herding sheep and cows
   B. manufacturing clothing
   C. farming oats and wheat
   D. trade of gold and salt

6. What is meant by the phrase "scramble for Africa"?
   A. Africans migrated to other countries in large numbers throughout the 1800s.
   B. South Africans cornered the diamond mines.
   C. Large numbers of Asians came to Africa in the 1800s.
   D. European powers competed with one another to gain African territory.

Africa Outcome Test (continued)

Use the map <u>and</u> your knowledge of social studies to answer question 7.

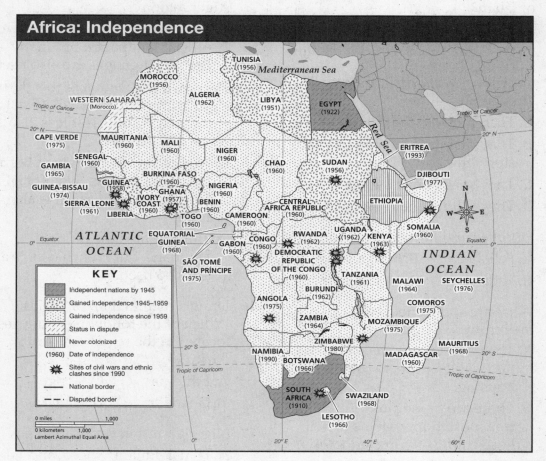

7. In what decade did most African countries gain their independence?

   A. 1950s   **C.** 1930s

   B. 1960s   **D.** 1940s

8. How have African countries tried to address their farming problems?

   A. By using traditional African farming methods

   B. By encouraging people to stop farming and move to the cities

   C. By developing hybrid plants and increasing crop size

   D. By bringing in more food from other countries

9. Why was nationalism important in Africa?

   A. Nationalism helped Africans accept their European rulers.

   B. Nationalism caused Africans to adopt European styles of government.

   C. Nationalism created movements for independence against imperial powers.

   D. Nationalism created democratic governments in every African country.

Africa Outcome Test (continued)

10. What is the name of the sacred book of Islam?

    A. the Bible   **C.** the Quran

    B. the Atlas   **D.** the Five Pillars

11. How have West Africans kept their strong cultural ties?

    A. They move to the cities.

    B. They maintain kinship ties and storytelling traditions.

    C. They speak one language.

    D. They follow one religion.

12. Egypt's rural farmers are called

    A. Fellaheen   **B.** Berbers

    C. Bazaars   **D.** Nomads

13. What are some effects of overcrowding in Cairo?

    A. The government has made noticeable efforts to provide housing.

    B. There are numerous transportation systems to help keep traffic moving smoothly.

    C. There are plans to create new cities in the southern part of Egypt.

    D. There are traffic jams and housing shortages.

14. Most people in Algeria live

    A. along the coastal region.

    B. in the desert.

    C. along the Nile.

    D. in the Sahel.

15. What languages are spoken in Algeria today?

    A. Arabic and French are the two official languages, but many Berber languages are also used.

    B. French and Tamazight, a Berber language, are the two official languages, but Arabic is also used.

    C. Arabic and Tamazight, a Berber language, are the two official languages, but French is also used.

    D. Tamazight is the official language, but French and Arabic are also used.

16. Draw a mental map of Africa. Which of the following countries is located in the region of West Africa?

    A. Ethiopia   **C.** Congo

    B. Ghana   **D.** Algeria

17. Nigeria's ethnic groups include

    A. Hausa-Fulani, Xhosa, and Igbo.

    B. Xhosa, Yoruba, and Igbo.

    C. Hausa-Fulani, Yoruba, and Igbo.

    D. Hausa-Fulani, Yoruba, and Xhosa.

18. In what ways did Julius Nyerere change Tanzania by the time he had stepped down as president?

    A. There were multiple national languages and the economy was prospering.

    B. There was one national language but the economy was still struggling.

    C. The ujamaa villages had become successful.

    D. The literacy rate declined.

Africa Outcome Test *(continued)*

19. What is the source for most of the wealth in the Congo?

   A. Mining of diamonds, oil, and copper

   B. Trade of salt and gold

   C. Farming of tea and cacao beans

   D. Fishing

20. Why was the election of Nelson Mandela as president of South Africa a significant event?

   A. He was the first Afrikaner president of South Africa.

   B. He had led the country to independence from Great Britain.

   C. He was the first black African president after apartheid ended.

   D. He had been living abroad in the United States.

Directions: *Read each question. Write your response on the lines provided.*

21. Briefly describe the ways in which urbanization is changing traditional family life in West Africa.

_____

_____

_____

_____

22. Briefly describe some of the effects of overcrowding in the city of Cairo.

_____

_____

_____

_____

Africa Outcome Test (continued)

Read the following statement and then answer question 23.

Tell him that
We do not wish greediness
We do not wish that he should curse us
We do not wish that his ears should be hard of hearing
We do not wish that he should call people fools
We do not wish that he should act on his own initiative [act alone]
We do not wish that it should ever be said 'I have no time I have no time.'
We do not wish personal abuse
We do not wish personal violence.
   —Akan statement of political expectation

23. The Akan are the largest ethnic group in Ghana. Discuss how this statement reflects the beliefs of the people of Ghana. Did Kwame Nkrumah and other subsequent presidents of Ghana seem to follow the Akan advice?

_____

_____

_____

_____

24. Briefly describe some of the advantages and disadvantages of a one-party political system.

_____

_____

_____

_____

Africa Outcome Test (continued)

25. Write an essay discussing why it was important that South Africa end apartheid and how South Africa has changed since the end of apartheid.

_____

_____

_____

_____

_____

_____

_____

_____

_____

_____

_____

_____

_____

_____

_____

_____

_____

_____

_____

_____

_____

_____

_____

_____

Asia and the Pacific Outcome Test

Directions: *Read each question and choose the best answer. Then mark the letter for the answer you have chosen.*

Use the map <u>and</u> your knowledge of social studies to answer question 1.

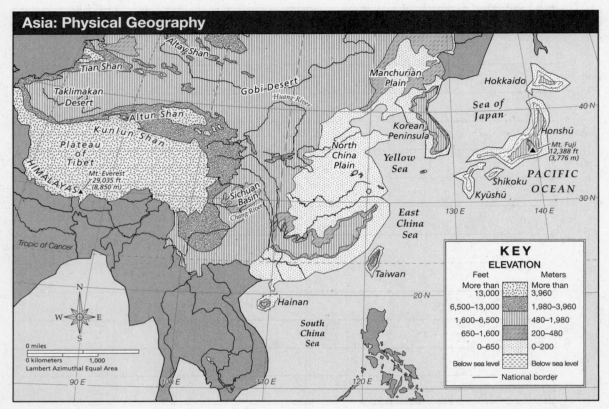

Asia: Physical Geography

1. Which of the following statements best describes the physical geography of China?

   A. More than one-half of the land is flat, rolling plains with a low elevation.

   B. Earthquakes and volcanoes created the country's unique landscape.

   C. More than two-thirds of the land is made up of mountains and deserts.

   D. The country is an archipelago made up of four large islands.

2. The Rub' al-Khali on the Arabian Peninsulas is called the "Empty Quarter." Why?

   A. The forest is protected and cannot be developed.

   B. Almost nothing lives in this flat, hot territory.

   C. It takes up three-quarters of the Arabian Peninsula.

   D. One quarter of the residents died in a plague.

Asia and the Pacific Outcome Test *(continued)*

3. What is one effect of Australia and New Zealand's isolated location on the development of animal and plant life?

   A. Most of their animals and plants are found all over the world.

   B. Many of their animals and plants are found nowhere else on Earth.

   C. Many of their animals and plants require little water to survive.

   D. Many of their animals and plants are found on islands in the Pacific and Atlantic oceans.

4. What role does climate play in the economy of New Zealand?

   A. Because of a hot, dry climate, New Zealand faces constant problems in trying to create a diverse economy that does not rely on agriculture.

   B. The climate of New Zealand prevents farmers from raising sheep and cattle, which would greatly improve the economy.

   C. The climate of New Zealand has extreme temperature changes; therefore, the country cannot depend on income from farming.

   D. Because New Zealand has a mild climate and plenty of rainfall, agriculture is an important part of the economy.

5. By the late 1700s, much of the Indian subcontinent had come under the rule of which European nation?

   A. Spain

   B. Germany

   C. Great Britain

   D. Italy

Use the passage and your knowledge of social studies to answer the following question.

> If the robber is not caught, the man who has been robbed shall formally declare whatever he has lost… and the city and the mayor…shall replace whatever he has lost for him
> —*from Hammurabi's Code*

6. Based on the passage, what is significant about Hammurabi's Code?

   A. It was used to translate the Rosetta Stone.

   B. It let citizens know their rights.

   C. It was only a list of punishments for crimes.

   D. Scholars today do not believe it was significant.

7. The majority of people in Central Asia follow which religion?

   A. Islam   C. Judaism

   B. Christianity   D. Buddhism

8. Why did the United States support South Vietnam during Vietnam's civil war?

   A. France was supporting North Vietnam.

   B. The United States wanted South Vietnam's Communist government to gain power.

   C. France was also supporting South Vietnam.

   D. The United States wanted to keep North Vietnam's Communist government from gaining power.

Asia and the Pacific Outcome Test (continued)

9. Which statement best describes the role of other countries in the history of the Pacific island nations?

   A. Because of their proximity to the islands, Australia and New Zealand have fought bitterly with the islanders over culture, traditions, and religion.

   B. The first people to stay on the islands came from Japan, and Japanese culture continues to play an important role in islanders' lives today.

   C. After World War II, most Pacific islands gained independence, and their traditional cultures blended with the cultures of other countries.

   D. Because the islands are so secluded from larger landmasses, islanders must depend on imports for most of their agricultural goods.

10. How did free enterprise help improve China's economy?

    A. China established several national banks that helped the economy of its southern neighbors.

    B. The government allowed the Chinese to choose their own jobs and regulated their income in order to distribute it equally.

    C. Private business produced 75 percent of China's gross domestic product.

    D. Everyone in China could choose their own jobs, start private businesses, and make a profit.

11. India's major exports include gemstones, jewelry, textiles, and

    A. automobiles.

    B. computer software.

    C. wheat.

    D. wood and wood products.

12. What is one of the main problems with exporting oil and gas from Kazakhstan and Turkmenistan?

    A. These countries are landlocked, with no direct access to the sea.

    B. These countries are not interested in exporting their resources.

    C. Foreign companies are not interested in developing these resources.

    D. Oil and gas resources are in limited supply in these countries.

13. Which statement best describes Vietnam's economy?

    A. Vietnam's communist government does not allow any free enterprise.

    B. Vietnamese living in rural areas enjoy greater prosperity than those living in cities.

    C. Despite some economic growth, Vietnam is one of the poorest nations in Asia.

    D. South Vietnam's economy is worse than Northern Vietnam's economy because South Vietnam has been much slower to modernize.

Asia and the Pacific Outcome Test *(continued)*

14. Which statement best describes the role the Huang river plays in China?

   A. The loess deposited by the Huang River creates one of the best farming areas in China.

   B. The Huang River is the transportation route between China and India.

   C. Severe pollution in the Huang River led to the creation of the Gobi desert.

   D. The Huang River is one of the few rivers in China that does not require dams to control flooding.

15. The Pacific islands lie in the tropics. This means they experience

   A. seasons that are the opposite of those in the Northern Hemisphere.

   B. mild winters and mild summers.

   C. year round temperatures in the 80s and mid 90s in degrees Fahrenheit.

   D. widely varying temperatures.

16. China is an ethnically diverse nation. Japan is a

   A. heterogeneous nation.

   B. diffused nation.

   C. nation of immigrants.

   D. homogeneous nation.

17. Two factors have affected Japan's labor force. One is the country's low birthrate. The other is

   A. mandatory military service.

   B. limited immigration.

   C. the switch from manufacturing to service industries.

   D. lack of natural resources.

18. What statement BEST describes the border between North Korea and South Korea?

   A. It is the most heavily armed border in the world.

   B. It was created by a natural barrier of mountains.

   C. It is the division between two former European colonies.

   D. There is no border. North and South Korea are a single country.

19. Rainfall is scarce in Pakistan, therefore farmers rely heavily on irrigation from the

   A. Ganges River.

   B. Deccan River.

   C. Indus River.

   D. Huang River.

20. Which statement BEST describes the government of Saudi Arabia?

   A. It is an absolute monarchy ruled under Islamic law.

   B. It is a democracy ruled under Islamic law.

   C. It is a republic ruled under Islamic law.

   D. It is a dictatorship ruled under Islamic law.

Asia and the Pacific Outcome Test (continued)

Directions: *Read each question and write your answer on the lines provided.*

21. Explain how China influenced the cultures of Korea, and Japan. What ideas were passed from one culture to another?

_____

_____

_____

_____

22. How did life change for the Aborigines of Australia and the Maori of New Zealand after the arrival of Europeans? What is life like today for these native peoples?

_____

_____

_____

_____

23. Explain how physical geography has impacted South Asia. Be sure to include the Himalayas, and the Indus and Ganges rivers in your answer.

_____

_____

_____

_____

24. Briefly describe how Taiwan's economy differs from the economy of China.

_____

_____

_____

_____

Asia and the Pacific Outcome Test (continued)

25. Write an essay comparing Buddhism and Hinduism. Include in your essay key figures, beliefs, and where Buddhism and Hinduism are practiced today.

_____

_____

_____

_____

_____

_____

_____

_____

_____

_____

_____

_____

_____

_____

_____

_____

_____

_____

_____

_____

_____

_____

_____

_____

_____

_____

_____

_____

_____

_____

The Ancient World Outcome Test

Directions: *Read each question and choose the best answer. Then mark the letter for the answer you have chosen.*

1. What were the advantages of a settled, farming life for early humans?

   A. Farming was much easier than hunting and gathering.

   B. They could move away from cities.

   C. They could move from place to place searching for food.

   D. They had a steady, year-round supply of food.

2. Food surpluses allowed ancient people

   A. to have time to play.

   B. to learn new skills and crafts.

   C. to read books.

   D. to learn how to read.

3. The oldest known written language is

   A. Sumerian.

   B. Sanskrit.

   C. Hieroglyphs.

   D. Chinese.

4. In the 500s B.C., Siddartha Gautama traveled around India in search of the meaning of life. Later, his teachings became known as Buddhism. Today, Buddhism is

   A. still India's main religion.

   B. no longer practiced.

   C. the main religion of Western Europe and the United States.

   D. no longer practiced much in India, but a major religion for many other Asian countries.

Use the map and your knowledge of social studies to answer the following question.

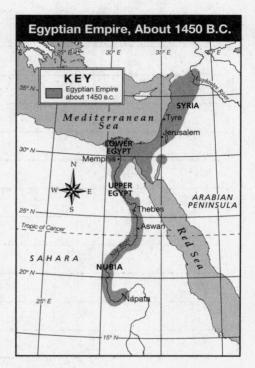

5. Memphis is located

   A. near Nubia.

   B. near the Mediterranean.

   C. in the Arabian peninsula.

   D. south of the Tropic of Cancer.

6. Ancient Egyptians believed that Amon-Re

   A. protected only the rich.

   B. protected only the poor.

   C. protected rich and poor alike.

   D. protected only men.

7. Egypt's pyramids were used

   A. to encourage order in society.

   B. to keep plebians busy.

   C. to protect Memphis.

   D. to ensure a pharaoh's place in the afterlife.

The Ancient World Outcome Test (continued)

8. Besides the Himalayas, the other mountain range north of India is called
   A. Nepal.
   B. Hindu Kush.
   C. Pakistan.
   D. Indus.

9. To help control flooding, the early Chinese people chose to
   A. pray to their gods to spare them.
   B. plant trees near the rivers.
   C. build dikes.
   D. construct dams.

10. The teachings of Confucius
    A. have been lost.
    B. were written down by his son.
    C. influenced the rulers of China.
    D. influenced the rulers of India during his lifetime.

11. Shi Huangdi ordered the construction of the Great Wall in order to
    A. demonstrate his power.
    B. protect China from invaders.
    C. create an impressive tomb.
    D. join two kingdoms.

12. One achievement under the Han Dynasty was
    A. outlawing the ideas of Confuscius.
    B. the design and construction of the Great Wall.
    C. creating a common currency for all of China.
    D. Sima Qian's *Historical Records*.

13. One source of wealth for Athens was
    A. the personal fortunes of its leaders.
    B. tribute paid by weaker city-states.
    C. investments in stocks and bonds.
    D. the use of conquered people as free labor, or helots.

14. An agora is
    A. a place to fear.
    B. a street.
    C. a temple.
    D. a public market.

15. New tools and ideas spread from one society to another as
    A. people married into a different social class.
    B. rulers paid for technological information.
    C. people traded information along with goods.
    D. people tired of their own culture.

16. Geography and limited resources encouraged Phoenicians to
    A. become an agricultural society.
    B. limit contact with other nations.
    C. build pyramids as storage centers.
    D. become a great sea power.

The Ancient World Outcome Test (continued)

Use the map and your knowledge of social studies to answer questions 17-18.

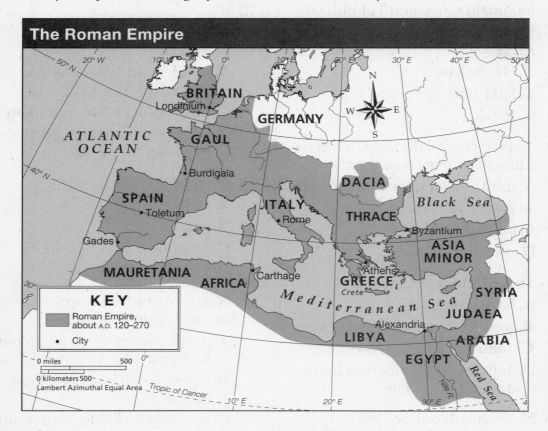

The Roman Empire

17. Greece is in what direction from Rome?

  A. northeast   **C.** east

  B. southeast   **D.** west

18. Byzantium later became Constantinople and the new capital of the Roman Empire. Why do you suppose the emperor Constantine chose this city?

  A. Its strategic location between the Black and Mediterranean seas.

  B. Its distance from Rome allowed Constantine freedom.

  C. Constantine probably chose it at random.

  D. Its easy access to the Atlantic Ocean.

19. The people of _____ depended on a regular pattern of summer and winter monsoons.

  A. Egypt

  B. India

  C. China

  D. Greece

20. Menes of Egypt and Chandragupta of India are known for

  A. uniting kingdoms.

  B. building hospitals.

  C. converting to Buddhism.

  D. allowing Rome to conquer their kingdoms.

The Ancient World Outcome Test (continued)

21. Describe the elements, such as government and culture, that characterize a civilization.

_____

_____

_____

_____

Use the map <u>and</u> your knowledge of social studies to answer question 22.

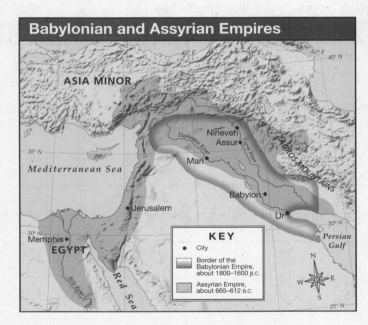

Babylonian and Assyrian Empires

22. Describe the pattern you see in the rise and fall of the many civilizations in Mesopotamia.

_____

_____

_____

_____

The Ancient World Outcome Test (continued)

23. Compare the social structure of the ancient Indian caste system to the Egyptian social structure which some describe as resembling a pyramid.

_____

_____

_____

_____

> No one suffers a penalty for what he thinks. No one may be forcibly removed from his own house. The burden of proof is upon the person who accuses. In inflicting penalties, the age and inexperience of the guilty party must be taken into account.
> —Code of Justinian

24. Read the passage above. Then write a paragraph comparing the Code of Justinian written during ancient Rome and our present-day system of justice.

_____

_____

_____

_____

Name _____ Class _____ Date_____

The Ancient World Outcome Test (continued)

25. Write an essay discussing the contributions of Greek and Roman civilization to Western culture.

_____

_____

_____

_____

_____

_____

_____

_____

_____

_____

_____

_____

_____

_____

_____

_____

_____

_____

_____

_____

_____

_____

_____

_____

_____

_____

Medieval Times to Today Outcome Test

Directions: *Read each question and choose the best answer. Then mark the letter for the answer you have chosen.*

Directions: *Use the map __and__ your knowledge of social studies to answer questions 1-2.*

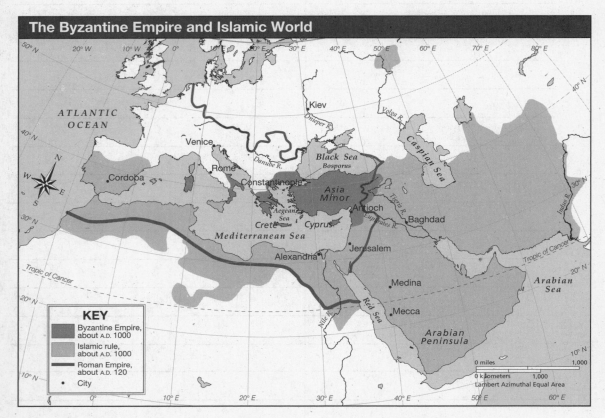

The Byzantine Empire and Islamic World

KEY
- Byzantine Empire, about A.D. 1000
- Islamic rule, about A.D. 1000
- Roman Empire, about A.D. 120
- • City

1. Which of the following describes Constantinople's location?

   A. It was located where the climate provided enough rain to keep its rivers and canals full.

   B. It was located where there was rich farmland to provide food for travelers.

   C. It was located at a crossroads of trade routes on land and sea.

   D. It was located close enough to Rome that Constantine could govern both cities.

2. What was the source of Constantinople's wealth?

   A. rich deposits of gold nearby

   B. the sale of slaves

   C. the production of religious icons for use in the churches

   D. taxes from trading goods that came into the city

3. The Five Pillars of Islam represent

   A. social classes in Muslim society.

   B. the five practices which are the foundation of Islam.

   C. the five points at which Muslim mosques must be supported.

   D. the five gods which Muslims worship.

Medieval Times to Today Outcome Test (continued)

4. Why did European historians know so little about the history of African civilizations south of the Sahara until recently?

   A. They weren't able to travel inland because of the mountains.

   B. The Sahara received too much rainfall, the forests were too thick to pass through.

   C. They were cut off from the area by the desert of the Sahara.

   D. The grasslands and savanna are similar to Europe so they had little interest in exploring.

5. Why was salt a valuable product for early civilizations in western Africa?

   A. People needed it to preserve food and for good health, and it was scarce in other areas.

   B. It was part of religious celebrations throughout much of Africa.

   C. Because it was common throughout all of Africa, people could use it as a form of money.

   D. It was used to prevent diseases carried by insects in the rainforests.

6. How did contact with Muslim traders around 1400 affect East African city-states, such as Kilwa?

   A. Diseases from the outside world killed a large number of East Africans.

   B. The Christian religion spread in East Africa.

   C. The Muslim traders took over the city-states.

   D. A new culture and language, called Swahili, developed.

7. How did the Incas of South America take advantage of the plentiful stone in their environment?

   A. They used it to create beautiful jewelry.

   B. They built large cathedrals in which to practice Christianity.

   C. They built roads, buildings, and aqueducts.

   D. They built the Colosseum.

8. Which of the following formed alliances in eastern North America to help keep peace?

   A. the Anasazi

   B. the Adena and Hopewell cultures

   C. the Iroquois nations

   D. the Plains Indians

9. Which of the following describes the Silk Road during the 700s?

   A. It served as the border between China and India to the south.

   B. Trade along it brought new goods and new ideas to China and spread Chinese ideas and goods.

   C. Traders were afraid to use it because the Mongols attacked the caravans.

   D. It connected the northern and southern areas of China and allowed grain to be delivered to the capital in the north.

Medieval Times to Today Outcome Test (continued)

10. Which of the following describes how Japan's geography affected the development of its culture?

   A. Mountains made land travel hard and sea travel important.

   B. Because the islands separated from Asia, most of its land is similar to China and the cultures developed in similar ways.

   C. Rich farmland along its rivers encouraged people to live in cities on their banks.

   D. Because of its many mountains, rain is scarce and people learned to use their water carefully.

11. During feudalism, noble women were

   A. required to weave a certain amount of cloth each year.

   B. kept in great luxury and had few responsibilities.

   C. part of the groups which advised the kings on taxes and military affairs.

   D. trained as ladies and expected to manage large households.

12. In 1095, Pope Urban II spoke the following words to a group in France: "You common people who have been miserable sinners, become soldiers of Christ! You nobles, do not [quarrel] with one another. Use your arms in a just war! Labor for everlasting reward." What was he referring to?

   A. the beginning of the Crusades to retake the Holy Land

   B. the beginning of the Hundred Years' War with England

   C. the beginning of the Reformation by Martin Luther

   D. the beginning of the Inquisition

13. Which of the following is an example of how artists used science to improve their work during the Renaissance?

   A. They developed new paints with brighter colors.

   B. They studied bones and muscles to understand how to portray people better.

   C. They changed how they painted the earth and the stars once they understood gravity.

   D. They were able to preserve their work better by using better frames and glass.

14. Which of the following are the countries which funded the most expeditions during the Age of Exploration?

   A. Spain, Portugal, France

   B. Spain, Portugal, England

   C. Spain, England, Italy

   D. Italy, Portugal, France

15. The ideas of the Enlightenment relied on

   A. new ideas from East Asia rather than traditional Western thinking.

   B. faith and religious teachings rather than reason and experience.

   C. traditional Western thinking rather than new ideas from East Asia.

   D. reason and experience rather than religion teaching and faith.

Medieval Times to Today Outcome Test *(continued)*

16. How did crop shortages in the late 1780s affect events in France?

A. The people looked to the king for help and supported him after he helped them get food.

B. It worsened the common people's resentment against unfair taxes and caused widespread riots.

C. The economy of France weakened so that there wasn't enough money to win the war with England.

D. The farmers across France lost their land and eventually formed a group to oppose the king.

17. Which of the following describes the relationship between the British empire in the 1760s and the Industrial Revolution?

A. Colonies provided raw materials for manufacturing and people to buy manufactured products.

B. Colonies slowed the changes of the Industrial Revolution because they required too much money to defend.

C. The Industrial Revolution began in British colonies where there was a large supply of workers.

D. The British gave up some of their colonies so they could concentrate on improving manufacturing techniques.

18. How did Napoleon's reign affect nationalism in Europe?

A. It discouraged many countries from learning about nationalism or supporting it.

B. It divided much of Europe into areas where people worshipped different religions.

C. It encouraged pride in France as a nation and led other countries to rebel against French rule.

D. It forced nations to form alliances for their own protection.

19. What did Lenin do after the Russian czar was forced to give up power in 1917?

A. He had to leave the country to avoid assassination.

B. He took control and began a Communist government.

C. He continued fighting in World War I until Russia was finally defeated by Germany.

D. He changed the government to a democracy, but was soon overthrown by Stalin.

20. Mohandas Gandhi is famous for

A. opposing communism in Eastern Europe and Africa.

B. helping countries in the Middle East fight terrorism.

C. preventing India from breaking up into smaller countries.

D. leading India to independence through nonviolence.

Medieval Times to Today Outcome Test *(continued)*

21. How were the governments of the Incan and the Aztec Empires similar?

_____

_____

_____

_____

22. Why did the Tokugawa shogunate isolate Japan from foreign influences? How did they go about doing this?

_____

_____

_____

_____

23. Peter the Great ruled Russia in the early 1700s and wanted to gain control of a port on the Black Sea to the south. Why did he want a port there and how might it have affected Russia at the time?

_____

_____

_____

_____

24. Briefly describe what is meant by a "global economy" and give an example of how it might work today.

_____

_____

_____

_____

Medieval Times to Today Outcome Test (continued)

25. Before she became Queen of England in 1558, Elizabeth I wrote the following:

" . . . what a . . . ship [is] without a pilot, a flock without a shepherd, a body without a head, the same, I think, is a kingdom without the health and safety of a good monarch."

How does this statement reflect people's beliefs about monarchs at the time? Write a short, three-paragraph essay that includes how the power of monarchs grew after the end of feudalism, the rights and powers of monarchs in Europe during the 1400s-1700s, and how the role of monarchs changed during the Enlightenment and later political revolutions.

_____

_____

_____

_____

_____

_____

_____

_____

_____

_____

_____

_____

_____

_____

_____

_____

_____

_____

_____

Foundations of Geography Outcome Test Answer Key

1. C (NG 14)

2. B (NG 1)

3. A (NG 7)

4. D (NG 7)

5. C (NG 15)

6. C (NG 2)

7. C (NG 9)

8. A (NG 17)

9. B (NG 10)

10. C (NG 14)

11. A (NG 6)

12. B (NG 10

13. C (NG 16)

14. B (NG 11)

15. B (NG 14)

16. B (NG 18)

17. D (NG 4, 5)

18. B (NG 2, 3)

19. A (NG 11, 16)

20. B (NG 10, 12)

21. As Earth rotates on its axis, the time of day or night changes. The time difference is a few seconds per mile. Governments have divided the world into standard time zones. The times in neighboring zones are one hour apart. (NG 5)

22. Students answers will vary, but may include: forces inside Earth, such as magma, volcanoes, earthquakes, and moving plates. Students may also write about weathering and erosion. (NG 7, 17, 18)

23. The graph shows that the world population, which had grown only slowly in the centuries following 1200, has grown very rapidly in the past century. Some of the problems associated with this rapid growth are lack of employment, lack of schools, scarcity of decent housing, and inadequate public services. (NG 9)

24. Students will describe two of the seven types of government listed. (NG 13)

25. Student answers will vary. Accept answers that have a clear topic sentence and specific supporting sentences. (NG 14)

The United States and Canada Outcome Test
Answer Key

1. B (NG 3)   11. B (NG 11)

2. A (NG 7)   12. C (NG 11)

3. D (NG 8)   13. D (NG 12)

4. B (NG 9)   14. D (NG 9)

5. D (NG 11)   15. A (NG 6)

6. C (NG 9)   16. D (NG 9)

7. C (NG 9)   17. D (NG 2,13)

8. D (NG 14)   18. A (NG 2, 4)

9. A (NG 3)   19. B (NG 11, 12)

10. A (NG 17)   20. C (NG 11, 18)

21. Students should note that the temperature in Miami is consistently warmer than the temperature in Toronto. Students may discuss different kinds of work and recreation available in Miami and Toronto. (NG 4)

22. Answers will vary, but may include: similarities are both the United States and Canada have central governments, a constitution and citizens elect their leaders. The differences are the British monarch is the formal head of state in Canada. The head of government is a prime minister. In the United States, the president is both. (NG 12)

23. Answers will vary, but may include: during the Revolutionary War, the United States attempted a plan for government called the Articles of Confederation that had failed. This time, the states agreed to form a stronger central government and wrote the Constitution, which set up the framework for our current federal government. (NG 13)

24. Manifest Destiny was the belief that the United States had the right to own all the land from the Atlantic to the Pacific. This belief was used to justify westward expansion. (NG 12)

25. Answers will vary, but may include: as immigrants travel to America, they bring pieces of their own culture with them. Over the years, different people have brought different pieces of many different cultures. All these pieces are what make America so diverse. Students' essays should have a clear topic sentence and give specific supporting details about American diversity. (NG 9, 11)

Latin America Outcome Test
Answer Key

1. A (NG 5, 7)

2. D (NG 3, 4, 8)

3. B (NG 11, 15, 16)

4. C (NG 9, 13)

5. C (NG 9, 12)

6. C (NG 6, 11)

7. D (NG 4, 9, 10)

8. A (NG 4, 9, 10)

9. B (NG 9, 12)

10. C (NG 1, 3, 12)

11. C (NG 1, 3, 8, 9, 10, 12)

12. B (NG 13, 16)

13. A (NG 9, 16)

14. A (NG 13)

15. D (NG 2, 3, 4)

16. B (NG 4, 8, 9)

17. A (NG 4, 12, 14, 17, 18)

18. C (NG 2, 3, 4)

19. C (NG 2, 4)

20. D (NG 4, 11, 12)

21. The narrow isthmus made it possible to construct a canal. Colombia, which controlled the area, refused to let the United States build a canal. The U.S. helped Panama gain independence to build the canal. Today Panama is an international crossroads for trade. (NG 4, 5, 11, 13, 14, 17)

22. Spaniards had guns, cannons and horses. The Europeans also carried diseases to which the Native Americans had never been exposed. Also, because of local rivalries, some Native Americans were eager to help the Spanish conquistadors. (NG 13)

23. Chile is long and narrow with mountains, beaches, deserts, forests, and glaciers. (NG 2, 4)

24. Puerto Rico is a commonwealth of the United States. Puerto Ricans are American citizens. They cannot vote in presidential elections. They do not pay United States taxes and have only a nonvoting representative in the United States Congress. Puerto Ricans do serve in the armed forces of the United States. (NG 4, 13)

25. Students answers will vary. Accept answers that have a clear topic sentence and specific supporting sentences.

Europe and Russia Outcome Test
Answer Key

1. B (NG 9)	**11.** D (NG 16)
2. C (NG 12)	**12.** C (NG 16)
3. C (NG 9, 10, 13)	**13.** B (NG 13)
4. C (NG 12)	**14.** B (NG 12, 13)
5. A (NG 12)	**15.** D (NG 4)
6. A (NG 16)	**16.** B (NG 15)
7. D (NG 8)	**17.** A (NG 9)
8. C (NG 8)	**18.** C (NG 4)
9. A (NG 9, 10)	**19.** D (NG 13)
10. C (NG 9)	**20.** B (NG 14)

For the short answer and the essay questions, answers will vary, but may touch on the following points:

21. Answers will vary, but may include: reexamining Greek and Roman culture, an emphasis on the importance of human nature and human abilities, and using art to understand God, man, and nature. The printing press also increased the availability of books. (NG 10)

22. The economy of East Germany was very weak. The new government sold factories to private businesses, modernized factories and businesses, cleaned up toxic waste sites, and began producing more consumer goods, all of which were very costly. The government also moved the capital back to Berlin to aid in linking east and west. (NG 16)

23. Ukraine had been taken over by the Communist government of the Soviet Union. It changed farms to large collectives and used the food to feed people throughout the country. The people of Ukraine weren't allowed to keep much of the food they grew and many starved. (NG 16)

24. Gorbachev wanted to change the government to allow more freedoms and to reduce the government's control of the economy. Gorbachev was proposing that the government should change from the Communist system to a more democratic system. (NG 13)

25. Answers will vary. Accept answers that have a clear topic sentence and specific supporting sentences. (NG 5, 10, 11, 13, 16, 17)

Africa Outcome Test
Answer Key

1. A (NG 15)

2. C (NG 3, 8)

3. A (NG 6, 11)

4. B (NG 9, 17)

5. D (NG 16)

6. D (NG 3, 13)

7. B (NG 1)

8. C (NG 14, 18)

9. C (NG 12)

10. C (NG 9)

11. B (NG 4)

12. A (NG 9)

13. D (NG 9)

14. A (NG 3)

15. C (NG 4, 10)

16. B (NG 2)

17. C (NG 9)

18. B (NG 14)

19. A (NG 16)

20. C (NG 16)

21. Answers will vary, but may include: many young men looking for work travel long distances to West Africa's cities. The women often stay home and raise the children and farm the land. The men come home from time to time to visit their families. (NG 9, 10)

22. Answers will vary, but may include: traffic jams and housing shortages. Some people live in the tents that they have set up on boats on the Nile. Others live in homes they have built in the huge cemeteries on the outskirts of Cairo. Some farmland has been lost because people have had to build homes on it. (NG 4, 14)

23. Answers will vary, but may include: Akan's believe in a government where people have a say and want peace. Answers may point to the improvements that presidents of Ghana tried to make and have made. In general, the presidents have tried to do things that reflect Akan principles, but many of the people of Ghana felt that Nkrumah acted on his own initiative when he borrowed money to improve Ghana. (NG 6, 13)

24. Answers will vary, but may include: a one-party system can limit people's options. Limited options can increase corruption. On the other hand, multiple parties can make existing divides worse. Ethnic rivalries can become political rivalries and tear a country apart. The goal of a one party system is to bring people together. (NG 12)

25. Answers will vary. Accept answers that have a clear topic sentence and specific supporting sentences. (NG 10, 13)

Asia and the Pacific Outcome Test
Answer Key

1. C (NG 1)

2. B (NG 6)

3. B (NG 8)

4. D (NG 15)

5. C (NG 17)

6. B (NG 17)

7. A (NG 10)

8. D (NG 13)

9. C (NG 10)

10. C (NG 11)

11. B (NG 11)

12. A (NG 16)

13. C (NG 11)

14. A (NG 2, 4, 15)

15. C (NG 3)

16. D (NG 4, 5)

17. B (NG 9, 11, 16)

18. A (NG 2, 5, 13)

19. C (NG 15)

20. A (NG 10)

21. Answers will vary, but may include: some Chinese settled parts of Korea, introducing Chinese customs and knowledge to Korea. Japan accepted the use of Chinese characters to write Japanese. Dynasties ruled in China and Korea. Other examples might include Buddhism, Chinese inventions, and teachings of Confucius. (NG 2)

22. Answers will vary, but may include: both groups suffered hardships after the arrival of Europeans, including being forced to adopt European ways. The Aborigines were forced off their lands and forced to work on sheep and cattle stations. Life is better for these native peoples today, but they form a very small part of each country's population. (NG 13)

23. Answers will vary, but may include: the Himalayas form a natural barrier between South Asia and the rest of Asia. The Indus and the Ganges rivers carry water and minerals which support farming to the plains. These plains are fertile and heavily populated. The Himalayas protect South Asia from Asia's winter monsoons. Because South Asia extends into the Indian Ocean, summer monsoons bring much needed heavy rainfall. (NG 2, 4, 9, 12)

24. Answers will vary, but may include: China follows a Communist system, where the government controls the economy and owns businesses. Taiwan follows the free enterprise system and has grown dramatically. China is in the process of moving toward an economy with fewer government controls. (NG 11)

25. Answers will vary. Accept answers that have a clear topic sentence and specific supporting sentences. (NG 10)

The Ancient World Outcome Test
Answer Key

1. D (NG 17)

2. B (NG 9)

3. A (NG 10)

4. D (NG 10)

5. B (NG 1)

6. C (NG 10)

7. D (NG 9)

8. B (NG 4)

9. C (NG 14)

10. C (NG 10)

11. B (NG 13)

12. D (NG 9)

13. B (NG 11)

14. D (NG 4)

15. C (NG 1)

16. D (NG 2)

17. B (NG 17)

18. A (NG 11)

19. B (NG 15)

20. A (NG 13)

21. Answers will vary, but may include: physical geography, especially elements that isolate a people or require them to adapt, agriculture or how a people collect food (and water), trade, who moves in and out of the civilization, language, religion, and in what manner it is ruled. (NG 9, 12)

22. Babylonians conquered Mesopotamia, seizing control of wealth, weapons and trade. They made improvements like building roads. Over time, the empire shrunk and finally, was destroyed. Then, the Assyrians seized control of the wealth, weapons and trade. They made improvements like building a great library. Over time, they were overthrown, and the Babylonians reclaimed power. (NG 12, 13)

23. Egyptian society resembled a pyramid with the pharoah at the top, a small upper class next, then a larger middle class, and finally very large peasant base. The Indian caste system divided people into hundreds of different groups depending on what job a person had. Everyone had to stay in the same caste as their parents.

24. Answers will vary, but may include: both place the burden of proof on the accuser, consider the age of a person when punishing them, and allow for free thought. (NG 9)

25. Answers will vary. Accept answers that have a clear topic sentence and specific supporting sentences. (NG 10)

Medieval Times to Today Outcome Test
Answer Key

1. C (NG 1, 3)
2. D (NG 16, 17)
3. B (NG 10)
4. C (NG 6, 8)
5. A (NG 5, 16)
6. D (NG 4)
7. C (NG 4, 14)
8. C (NG 13)
9. B (NG 10, 11)
10. A (NG 7, 15)

11. D (NG 10)
12. A (NG 13)
13. B (NG 10)
14. B (NG 2, 4)
15. D (NG 10)
16. B (NG 13, 15, 17)
17. A (NG 16, 17)
18. C (NG 13)
19. B (NG 12)
20. D (NG 13)

21. Both were controlled by emperors who lived in great cities. People were required to pay taxes or work for the government. Some groups were treated unfairly and rebelled against the government or helped the Spanish. (NG 12)

22. The Tokugawa shogunate was worried that Europeans might try to conquer Japan. They outlawed Christianity and forced Europeans to leave. They closed Japan's ports, banning most foreign travel and trade. They even stopped the building of large ships. (NG 13)

23. Most of Russia's ports and waterways froze during the winter. Peter the Great wanted a port on the Black Sea because it wouldn't freeze. With a warm water port, Russia would be able to trade all year round. A year-round trading port improved the economy and added to Russia's wealth. (NG 16, 17)

24. A global economy means doing business across national borders. A company may have workers in many different countries and purchase and sell goods in many countries as well. Technology allows better communication and transportation regardless of geographic obstacles. (NG 16, 18)

25. Answers will vary. Accept answers that have a clear topic sentence and specific supporting sentences. (NG 4, 10, 12, 13)